CIRIA C624

London, 2004

Development and flood risk
– guidance for the construction industry

J W Lancaster	Arup
M Preene	Arup
C T Marshall	Arup

CIRIA *sharing knowledge ■ building best practice*

CIRIA, Classic House, 174–180 Old Street, London EC1V 9BP, UK.
Telephone: +44 (0)20 7549 3300   Fax: +44 (0)20 7253 0523
Email: enquiries@ciria.org   Web: www.ciria.org

Summary

This book provides guidance to developers and the construction industry on the implementation of good practice in the assessment and management of flood risk as part of the development process, and is intended to promote development that is sustainable in terms of flood risk.

This guidance describes the mechanisms and impacts of flooding, covering a wide range of causes of flooding including rivers, the sea, estuaries, groundwater, overland flow, artificial drainage systems and infrastructure failure. National planning policy guidance for development and flood risk in the United Kingdom is also included.

This is practical guidance with the aim of achieving a consistent approach to the implementation of planning guidance in relation to flood risk. Such an approach should allow developments to be planned and designed more efficiently.

This guide is intended for the construction industry, in particular developers, builders, designers and planners, but it is also intended to provide background information for other parties involved in the development process, including insurers, mortgage lenders and the owners and occupiers of developments.

Development and flood risk – guidance for the construction industry

Lancaster, J W; Preene, M; Marshall, C T

CIRIA

CIRIA C624   © CIRIA 2004   ISBN 0-86017-624-X   RP675

Keywords		
Coastal and marine, flooding, housing, land use planning, rivers and waterways, sustainable construction		

Reader interest	Classification	
Developers, planning authorities, house builders,planners, construction professionals	AVAILABILITY CONTENT STATUS USER	Unrestricted Advice/guidance Committee-guided Developers, builders, architects, planners, hydrologists, water scientists, water engineers, water managers

Published by CIRIA, Classic House, 174–180 Old Street, London EC1V 9BP, UK.

British Library Cataloguing in Publication Data
A catalogue record is available for this book from the British Library

USER GUIDE

	Part A — Introduction to flood risk and development	Part B — Flood risk assessment	Part C — Flood risk assessment toolkit	Part D — Appendices
OBJECTIVE	THE FLOODING PROBLEM	INTRODUCTION TO PROCESSES TO ASSESS AND MANAGE FLOOD RISK	PROCESS FLOWCHARTS	INFORMATION
USERS	Readers unfamiliar with flood risk issues	Readers already familiar with flood risk issues — Practitioners	Practitioners and experienced users	
APPLICATION	Background to issues of development and flood risk	Overview of the flood risk assessment (FRA) process and summary of key factors	Detailed guidance on the execution of flood risk assessments	Useful information

Part A — Chapters

Chapter 1 — Introduction

Flood risk and the construction industry

Objectives of the report

Structure of the report

Chapter 2 — Flooding – causes and mechanisms

What is flood risk?

Types of flooding:
- fluvial
- coastal
- estuarial
- groundwater
- overland flow
- drainage systems
- infrastructure failure

Impact of climate change

Chapter 3 — Developments and flooding

Types of development

Impact of flooding on development

Impact on flood risk resulting from development

Part B — Chapters

Chapter 4 — Flood risk assessment within the planning process

Flood risk in the planning process

The sequential test

Definition of flood risk zone

Roles and responsibilities

Chapter 5 — Flood risk assessment

Sustainable development and flood risk

Flood risk assessment (FRA) methods
- Level 1 FRA
- Level 2 FRA
- Level 3 FRA

Part C — Chapter

Chapter 6 — Flood risk assessment and toolkit

Flowcharts & checklists for flood risk assessments

Part D — Appendices

Appendix A1 — National arrangements for the control of development and flood risk

Appendices
A1.1 England
A1.2 Wales
A1.3 Scotland
A1.4 Northern Ireland

Guidance on:
- planning policy
- flood defence organisations
- consents

Appendix A2 — Technical guidance on flood risk assessment

Technical guidance
- Level 1 FRA
- Level 2 FRA
- Level 3 FRA

Appendix A3 — Mitigation measures for flood risk management

Key design considerations

Types of mitigation
- site selection
- development zoning
- raising floor levels
- land raising
- flood warning
- flood proofing
- design of channel and hydraulic structures
- flood defences
- developer contributions
- compensatory flood storage
- management of runoff
- pumping

Appendix A4 — Professional institutions

Contact details for:

Institution of Civil Engineers/British Hydrological Society

Chartered Institution of Water and Environmental Management

Appendix A5 — Summary risk register

Example risk register to be used in FRA reports

Acknowledgements

Research contractor

This report is the result of CIRIA Research Project 675 carried out under contract to CIRIA by Arup.

Authors

James Lancaster BSc(Hons) PhD MCIWEM
Dr Lancaster is a senior hydrologist at Arup and is actively involved in the assessment and management of flood risk for existing and proposed developments. He has particular expertise in hydrological and hydraulic modelling and has carried out flood risk assessments for a wide range of proposed developments.

Martin Preene BEng PhD CEng FICE MCIWEM CGeol FGS
Dr Preene is an associate director at Arup and is involved in projects in the water, geotechnical and environmental fields. He has particular expertise in the management of groundwater and water resource issues.

Clive Marshall BSc(Hons) PhD CEng FICE FCIWEM
Dr Marshall is a consultant to Arup, with more than 30 years' experience in hydrology and river engineering with river and water authorities in the United Kingdom.

Steering group

Following CIRIA's usual practice, the research project was guided by a steering group which comprised:

Co-chairs

Dave Brook	Office of the Deputy Prime Minister
Charlie Rickard	Independent consultant, formerly of Mott MacDonald

Attending members

Richard Ashley	University of Bradford
Steve Ball	English Partnerships
Jonathan Chapman	Environment Agency
Mike Evans	Newark and Sherwood District Council
James McConnell	House Builders Federation
Laurence Morgan	British Waterways
Graham Perrior	National House-Building Council (NHBC)
Mervyn Pettifor	Environment Agency
Santi Santhalingham	Highways Agency
David Thomas	Bedford Group of Drainage Boards
John Wickham	Norwich Union

Corresponding members

John Blanksby	University of Bradford
Chris Broadbent	Building Research Establishment
John Davison	Department of the Environment Northern Ireland
Mike Long	Hampshire County Council
Jane Milne	Association of British Insurers
Joe Nicholson	Department of the Agriculture and Rural Development Northern Ireland
David Noble	Association of Drainage Authorities
Mike Samways	Huntingdonshire District Council
Paul Ryles	Scottish Environment Protection Agency

CIRIA managers

CIRIA's research managers for the project were Marianne Scott and Elizabeth Holliday.

ACKNOWLEDGEMENTS

Project funders

The project was funded by:

CIRIA's core member funding
British Waterways
DTI Partners in Innovation (PII) programme
Office of the Deputy Prime Minister (OPDM)
Newark and Sherwood District Council
National House-Building Council (NHBC)

Photographs

The following organisations are thanked for their provision of photographic material:

Arup, Bedford Group Internal Drainage Board, City of Edinburgh Council, Environment Agency, Halcrow, Hamshire County Council, NHBC, Posford Haskoning.

Contributors

CIRIA and the authors are grateful for the help given to this project by the funders, the members of the steering group, and by the many individuals who were consulted and provided data. In particular, acknowledgement is given to the following:

Nicholas Adjei	JBA Consulting
Steve Allison	Environment Agency
Marc Becker	Scottish Environment Protection Agency
John Burns	Scottish Environment Protection Agency
David Cameron	Scottish Environment Protection Agency
Sebastian Catovsky	Association of British Insurers
Craig Elliott	CIRIA
Mark Fletcher	Arup
Roland Grzybek	Halcrow Group
Ben Hamer	Halcrow Group
Ruth Harvey	Arup
Jane Healey	Arup
Paul Hunt	Environment Agency
Dave Jones	Environment Agency
Matthew Keen	Environment Agency
Alex Lee	Jones Pike & Associates
Darren Leftley	British Waterways
Will McBain	Arup
Malcolm MacConnachie	Scottish Environment Protection Agency
Byron Miller	Association of British Insurers
Grant Moffatt	Environment Agency
Alice Morgan	Environment Agency
Ken Moss	Environment Agency
Fola Ogunyoye	Posford Haskoning
Andrew Pepper	ATPEC River Engineering Consultancy
Marc Pinnel	Symonds Group
Vin K Robinson	Environment Agency
Will Rogers	URS Corporation
Katie Slater	Environment Agency
Mark Smith	Arup
Suresh Surendan	Environment Agency
Charles Thompson	Environment Agency
David Wilkes	Environment Agency

And all attendees of the project consultation workshop.

CIRIA C624

5

The authors would also like to thank their colleagues at Arup for their help and support in the production of this report.

Consultation with the above does not necessarily imply that the contributors endorse all views expressed in the published guidance.

ACKNOWLEDGEMENTS

Contents

CONTENTS

FIGURES

TABLES

BOXES

CONTENTS

GLOSSARY

Terms	Definition
Adoption of sewers	The transfer of responsibility for the maintenance of a system of sewers to a sewerage undertaker.
Afflux	Increase in upstream flood level caused by an obstruction to flow in a water course or on a *flood plain*.
Annual probability	The estimated probability of a flood of given magnitude occurring or being exceeded in any year. Expressed as, for example, 1-in-100 chance or 1 per cent.
Antecedent conditions	The condition of a *catchment* area at the start of a rainfall event.
Aquifer	A source of *groundwater* comprising water-bearing rock, sand or gravel capable of yielding significant quantities of water.
Artificial drainage system	A constructed drainage system such as a drain, sewer or ditch.
Astronomical tide level	The tidal level resulting from the gravitational effects of (mainly) the sun and the moon.
Boundary condition	A specified variable, typically water level or flow, which is defined at the edge of the spatial extent of a model to allow the model to solve its governing equations.
Brownfield site	Any land or site that has been previously developed.
Catchment	The area contributing flow or *runoff* to a particular point on a watercourse.
Climate change	Long-term variations in global temperature and weather patterns both natural and as a result of human activity, primarily greenhouse gas emissions.
Coastal flooding	Flooding from the sea.
Culvert	Covered channel or pipe that forms a watercourse below ground level.
Design event	An historic or notional *flood event* of a given annual *flood probability*, against which the suitability of a proposed development is assessed and *mitigation measures*, if any, are designed.
Design flood level	The maximum estimated water level during the *design event*.
Development	The carrying out of building, engineering, mining or other operations in, on, over or under land or the making of any material change in the use of any buildings or other land.
Discharge	Rate of flow of water.
Environmental impact assessment	A technique used for identifying the environmental effects of development projects. As a result of European Union Directive 85/337/EEC (as amended 1997), this is a legislative procedure to be applied to the assessment of the environmental effects of certain public and private projects which are likely to have significant effects on the environment.
Estuarial flooding	Flooding from an estuary, where water level will be influenced by river flows and tidal conditions.

Field drainage	System of drains to control the *water table* in agricultural land.
Flap valve	A simple form of non-return valve, employing a hinged flap to prevent reverse flow. Used in this guide as a generic term for any device which prevents backflow of water up a watercourse or *artificial drainage system*.
Flood defence	Flood defence infrastructure, such as flood walls and embankments, intended to protect an area against flooding, to a specified *standard of protection*.
Flood defence agency	A generic term used in this guide to refer to the Environment Agency in England and Wales, the Scottish Environment Protection Agency in Scotland, and the Rivers Agency in Northern Ireland, together with *Internal Drainage Boards* and local authorities, acting in their role as technical advisors to *Local Planning Authorities* on flood risk issues.
Flood defence level	The level to which flood defences are constructed, that is the level of the top of flood walls and embankments, expressed relative to Ordnance Datum.
Flood event	A flooding incident characterised by its peak level or flow, or by its level or flow *hydrograph*.
Flood plain	Area of land that borders a watercourse, an estuary or the sea, over which water flows in time of flood, or would flow but for the presence of flood defences where they exist.
Flood storage	The temporary storage of excess *runoff* or river flow in ponds, basins, reservoirs or on the *flood plain*.
Flood probability	The estimated probability of a flood of given magnitude occurring or being exceeded in any specified time period. See also *annual flood probability*.
Flood risk	An expression of the combination of the *flood probability* and the magnitude of the potential consequences of the *flood event*.
Flood risk assessment	A study to assess the risk of a site or area flooding, and to assess the impact that any changes or development in the site or area will have on *flood risk*.
Flood storage	The temporary storage of excess *runoff* or river flow in ponds, basins, reservoirs or on the *flood plain* during a *flood event*.
Fluvial flooding	Flooding from a river or other watercourse.
Freeboard	The difference between the *flood defence level* and the *design flood level*.
Functional flood plain	Unobstructed areas of the *flood plain* where water regularly flows in time of flood.
Greenfield runoff rate	The rate of *runoff* that would occur from the site in its undeveloped (and therefore undisturbed) state.
Groundwater	Water in the ground, usually referring to water in the saturated zone below the *water table*.
Groundwater flooding	Flooding caused by *groundwater* escaping from the ground when the *water table* rises to or above ground level.
Hydrograph	A graph, that shows the variation with time of the level or *discharge* in a watercourse.

Indicative flood map	A map that delineates the areas estimated to be at risk of flooding during an event of specified *flood probability*. "Indicative" acknowledges that such maps give an indication of the areas at risk but, due to the scale of the exercise, they are not reliable for precise information in relation to individual sites.
Infiltration capacity	A soil characteristic determining or describing the maximum rate at which water can enter the soil.
Infrastructure failure	Structural, hydraulic, geotechnical, mechanical or operational failure of infrastructure which normally retains, transmits or controls the flow of water.
Internal drainage board	Body with powers and duties relating to *ordinary watercourses* within an *Internal Drainage District*.
Internal drainage district	An area of land designated as such by Defra, or a predecessor Ministry, on the grounds that it derives benefit or avoids danger as a result of drainage operations.
Land drain	Drain used in agriculture to control the *water table* and reduce the frequency with which land becomes waterlogged.
Local planning authority	Body responsible for planning and controlling *development*, through the planning system
Main river	A watercourse designated on a statutory map of main rivers, maintained by Defra.
Material consideration	Matters which need to be taken into account by a planning authority when determining an application for planning permission.
Mitigation measure	A generic term used in this guide to refer to an element of *development* design which may be used to manage *flood risk* to the *development*, or to avoid an increase in *flood risk* elsewhere.
Ordinary watercourse	A watercourse which is not a private drain and is not designated a *main river*.
Overland flow flooding	Flooding caused by surface water *runoff* when rainfall intensity exceeds the infiltration capacity of the ground, or when the soil is so saturated that it cannot accept any more water.
Penstock	A sluice or gate used to control the flow of water.
Precautionary principle	The approach, to be used in the assessment of *flood risk*, which requires that lack of full scientific certainty shall not be used as a reason for postponing cost-effective measures to avoid or manage *flood risk*.
Passive flood plain	Areas that are within the "natural" *flood plain* but are not now subject to frequent flooding, because of the presence of flood alleviation measures.
Return period	A term sometimes used to express *flood probability*. It refers to the estimated average time gap between floods of a given magnitude, but as such floods are likely to occur very irregularly, an expression of the *annual flood probability* is to be preferred.
River flooding	See *fluvial flooding*.
Runoff	The flow of water, caused by rainfall, from an area.
Sea defences	Engineered structure designed to prevent *coastal flooding*.

Sequential test	A risk-based approach to *flood risk assessment*, applied through the use of *flood risk* zoning, where the type of *development* that is acceptable in a given zone is dependent on the assessed *flood risk* of that zone.
Sewer flooding	Flooding caused by the blockage or overflowing of sewers or urban drainage systems.
Standard of protection	The estimated probability of a *design event* occurring, or being exceeded, in any year. Thus it is the estimated probability of an event occurring which is more severe than those against which an area is protected by *flood defences*.
Strategic flood risk assessment	A study to examine *flood risk* issues on a sub-regional scale, typically for a river *catchment* or local authority area during the preparation of a development plan.
SUDS	See *sustainable drainage systems*.
Sustainable drainage systems	A sequence of management practices and control structures, often referred to as SUDS, designed to drain surface water in a more sustainable manner than some conventional techniques. Typically, these techniques are used to attenuate rates of *runoff* from *development* sites.
Sustainable development	Development which meets the needs of the present without compromising the ability of future generations to meet their own needs.
Tidal surge	An increase in tidal water level above the *astronomical tide level* caused by low barometric pressure and/or wind acting on the surface of the sea.
Tidelocking	The situation where a watercourse that drains to the sea, estuary or other watercourse cannot discharge at times of high water levels in the sea, estuary or other watercourse.
Wader scrape	A shallow depression in the ground providing habitat for wading birds
Water table	The level of *groundwater* in soil and rock, below which the ground is saturated.
Wetlands	An area where saturation or repeated inundation of water is the determining factor in the nature of the plants and animals living there.

ABBREVIATIONS

Abbreviation	Definition
ABI	Association of British Insurers
ADAS	Agricultural Drainage Advisory Service
AOD	Above Ordnance Datum
BGS	British Geological Survey
BHS	British Hydrological Society
BSI	British Standards Institution
CFMP	Catchment Flood Management Plan
CHAMP	Coastal Habitat Management Plan
CIWEM	Chartered Institution of Water and Environmental Management
COSLA	Committee of Scottish Local Authorities
Defra	Department for Environment, Food and Rural Affairs
DTLR	Department for Transport, Local Government and the Regions
FDA	Flood Defence Agency
FEH	Flood Estimation Handbook
FRA	Flood Risk Assessment
HOST	Hydrology of Soil Types
ICE	Institution of Civil Engineers
IDB	Internal Drainage Board
IDD	Internal Drainage District
LPA	Local Planning Authority
NERC	Natural Environment Research Council
ODPM	Office of the Deputy Prime Minister
OS	Ordnance Survey
PPG25	Planning Policy Guidance Note 25: Development and Flood Risk
PPW	Planning Policy Wales
RA	Rivers Agency
SEPA	Scottish Environment Protection Agency
SFRA	Strategic Flood Risk Assessment
SPP7	Scottish Planning Policy 7: Planning and Flooding
SSSI	Site of Special Scientific Interest
SUDS	Sustainable Drainage Systems
TAN15	Technical Advice Note (Wales) 15: Development and Flood Risk
UDP	Unitary Development Plan
UKCIP	United Kingdom Climate Impacts Programme
WHO	World Health Organisation
WRAP	Winter Rainfall Acceptance Potential.

1 Introduction

1.1 FLOOD RISK AND THE CONSTRUCTION INDUSTRY

Flooding is a major issue in the United Kingdom. The impacts of flooding can be devastating in terms of the cost of repairs, replacement of damaged property and loss of business. In addition the nuisance and stress caused by a flood event and clean-up operations, use of temporary accommodation and the general disruption, can be just as significant. In some circumstances there can be a very real risk to life, as exemplified by the floods on the UK east coast in 1953, when 307 people died.

The 1990s and early 2000s have seen the United Kingdom affected by several major flooding events which have caused considerable damage and, unfortunately, some loss of life. Similar events will almost certainly occur again and may be more frequent.

It is now widely recognised that the risk of flooding is a material planning issue that should be considered by planning authorities, developers and the construction industry for a wide range of locations and development types, and not merely in obvious flood plain areas. Less widely appreciated is the possibility that the development of a particular site may increase the flood risk elsewhere.

Within the United Kingdom, national planning policies provide guidance on how flood risk should be considered at all stages of the planning process, so that future damage to property and loss of life can be minimised. In principle, these policies require that:

- a risk-based approach be taken to avoid flood risk where possible, or otherwise to manage it appropriately

- the importance of flood plains be recognised, and development directed away from undeveloped and undefended flood plains

- developers should fund the provision and maintenance of flood risk mitigation measures that are required because of a development

- flood risk assessment and management should not be restricted to flood plains but should be applied on a catchment-wide basis, for the full range of flood mechanisms including groundwater and overland flow.

Population growth and demographic changes will contribute to increased pressure to construct developments which will be at risk of flooding, or which may increase the risk of flooding elsewhere. Climate change may mean that some areas previously considered to be at a low risk of flooding will be subject to significant flood risk in the future.

For development to be sustainable, planners and the construction industry will need to be able to assess flood risk and, if appropriate, identify what measures may be used to manage flood risk, when considering the appropriateness of proposed developments.

1.1.1 Responsibility of the construction industry for flood risk assessment

Those proposing specific developments are responsible for:

- providing an assessment of whether any proposed development is likely to be affected by flooding and whether it will affect flood risk elsewhere

- satisfying the planning authorities that any flood risk to the development or additional risk arising from the proposal will be successfully managed with minimum environmental effect, to ensure the site can be developed and used safely.

The construction industry should address these responsibilities in an efficient and consistent manner. The process through which these issues are dealt with is known as flood risk assessment (FRA).

The flood risk assessments prepared by, or on behalf of, the developer will be used by the local planning authority, who will be advised by the flood defence agency and other relevant organisations, as part of the determination of an application for planning permission.

1.2 OBJECTIVES OF THIS GUIDE

This guide provides guidance to developers and the construction industry on the implementation of good practice in relation to flood risk in the development process. It is intended to:

- promote sustainable development in relation to flood risk issues

- provide the construction industry with a consistent approach to implementing planning guidance relating to flood risk

- provide a means for developments to be planned and designed more efficiently

- identify a wide range of causes of flooding, not only from rivers and other watercourses, but also from the sea, estuaries, groundwater, overland flow, artificial drainage systems, and infrastructure failure.

- describe the effects of flooding on developments, and how developments can affect the risk of flooding elsewhere

- describe planning issues associated with the interaction between flood risk and development, and highlight the resulting challenges to the construction industry

- provide practical guidance for carrying out flood risk assessments

- provide advice and information on measures that can be used to manage flood risk and to satisfy flood-related planning conditions properly and efficiently.

This guide is intended for the construction industry as a whole and in particular for developers, builders, designers and planners, but it is also intended to provide background information for other parties involved in the development process, including insurers, mortgage lenders and the owners and occupiers of developments.

1.3 LIMITATIONS OF THIS GUIDE

The information in this guide is applicable across the United Kingdom as a framework to assess flood risk. However, different national planning policy guidance for flood risk exists in England, Scotland, Wales and Northern Ireland, and the specific requirements of these should be taken into account, based on the site location. The flood defence agency will also vary depending on site location. Further details are given in Appendices A1 to A4.

This guide is based on the planning guidance and legislation in place in March 2004. The reader should ensure that compliance is achieved with the guidance current at any future relevant date.

This guide is intended to assist those working in the construction industry to understand the need for, and the objectives of, flood risk assessments. It also provides general guidance about the planning system and methods of assessing and, if necessary, mitigating flood risk to, or caused by, developments. However, it cannot cover all possible circumstances and site conditions and is not a substitute for expert advice, or for timely consultation with the relevant local planning authority and flood defence agency.

1.4 STRUCTURE OF THE GUIDE

This guide is divided into four parts:

Part A: Introduction to flood risk and development.

Part B: Flood risk assessment.

Part C: Flood risk assessment toolkit.

Part D: Appendices.

A quick reference tool for where to find information is given in the "users' guide" on page 3.

Part A provides a brief background to the issues associated with development and flood risk, and is intended to be used by the non-expert who may be unfamiliar with flood risk issues. Within Part A there are two chapters:

Chapter 2 describes the background to flooding, and flood risk and the mechanisms of various types of flooding. The sources of flooding considered include rivers and other watercourses, the sea, estuaries, groundwater, overland flow, artificial drainage systems and infrastructure failure. The likely impact of climate change on flood risk is also discussed.

Chapter 3 outlines the interactions between developments and flooding. The economic, social, heath and safety, and environmental impacts of flooding on developments are described as well as the ways that developments can affect flood risk elsewhere.

Part B includes an overview of the flood risk assessment (FRA) process, including the approach taken to managing flood risk under the United Kingdom's legislative planning systems, and the recommended approach to FRAs. This part is intended to act as a summary of key factors, useful for those readers who are already familiar with the importance of flood risk issues. Within Part B there are two chapters:

Chapter 4 provides an overview of the planning process as it relates to flood risk. It describes the roles of key parties in the planning process and outlines the responsibility of the developer.

Chapter 5 provides brief practical guidance on carrying out flood risk assessments as part of the development and planning process.

Part C is a flood risk assessment toolkit. Part C comprises one chapter:

Chapter 6 provides a summary of the flood risk assessment process and contains flowcharts and checklists summarising a suitable approach to assessing flood risk for a wide range of conditions. The toolkit is intended to be of use to the practitioner conducting FRAs.

Part D contains appendices giving more detailed information on national planning policy guidance on flood risk, technical guidance on FRA, technical guidance on mitigation measures, relevant professional institutions and suggested formats for risk registers. A list of references is included.

The **CD-ROM** – included in the back cover of this guide – contains **Part C: flood risk assessment toolkit.** The guide and the toolkit can both be downloaded from the CIRIA website <www.ciria.org>.

1.5   RELATED GUIDANCE

Provision of guidance on flooding and flood risk is an important part of CIRIA's ongoing research. Information can be found on CIRIA's flooding website at <www.ciria.org/flooding>.

The following related CIRIA documents are available.

Design of Flood Storage Reservoirs, Book 14 (Hall *et al*, 1993).

Sustainable Urban Drainage Systems – best practice manual for England, Scotland, Wales and Northern Ireland, C523 (Martin *et al*, 2001).

Sustainable Drainage Systems. Hydraulic, structural and water quality advice, C609 (Wilson, Bray and Cooper), 2004.

Reducing the impacts of flooding – extemporary measures, FR/IP/45 (Elliott and Leggett, 2001).

Standards for the repair of buildings following flooding, C623 (to be published in 2004).

There is also a series of pamphlets jointly produced by the Environment Agency and CIRIA:

Flood products. Using flood protection products – a guide for homeowners.

After a flood. How to restore your home.

Damage limitation. How to make your home flood resistant.

HR Wallingford is currently undertaking a Defra/Environment Agency research project *Flood risk assessment guidance for new development* (research project FD2320). It is anticipated that this project will deliver additional tools and guidance to aid the flood risk assessment process, and the final project outputs are expected to be available in spring 2005.

Part A

INTRODUCTION TO FLOOD RISK AND DEVELOPMENT

Part

A

2 Flooding – causes and mechanisms

2.1 WHAT IS FLOOD RISK?

Flooding can result from a wide range of events and processes. Flooding occurs naturally, when specific environmental factors or combinations of factors occur. These factors can be diverse and site specific, and can include heavy rain, tidal surges and raised groundwater levels, among others. Flooding can also result from human interference with natural processes, such as changes to river channels, increases in runoff from land or blocked drainage systems. Flooding becomes a problem only when it has an adverse impact on people, property, infrastructure or the environment.

The challenge for the construction industry is to carry out development in a sustainable manner by managing the risk of flooding so that it does not have an unacceptable impact on a given site, and to ensure that developments do not increase flood risk elsewhere. A site that is appropriately located and designed, having regard to assessed flood risk, will experience little or no detrimental impacts during most flood events, and should not cause other areas to be at greater risk of flooding.

This chapter describes the concept of flood risk and defines flood probability. It outlines the diverse range of flooding events that can affect a development, and describes the mechanisms that can cause such events. The likely effects of climate change on flood risk are summarised.

2.1.1 The problem of flooding

Flooding is not a new problem, and there are records of people and property in the United Kingdom being affected by flooding throughout history. Flooding of a watercourse's flood plain is a natural process which, in the absence of defences, may occur periodically, perhaps every year. Similarly, low-lying land alongside estuaries and coastal areas may naturally flood as a result of storms and high tides and low-lying, poorly drained areas may periodically flood due to high groundwater levels. In many areas such flooding can provide increased biodiversity through the maintenance of flood plain habitats, but in agricultural areas it may lead to loss of agricultural productivity. However, **the major problem of flooding occurs when homes, businesses and transport infrastructure are built in areas subject to flood risk.**

For new development, in addition to the risk of the site itself flooding, the impact of the site on the risk of flooding elsewhere must also be considered. For example, increased areas of impermeable surfacing and roofing on a new development can increase the volume and rate of surface water runoff during storms, which may create or exacerbate flooding problems on other sites downstream.

Development located within a flood plain will generally be at significant risk of flooding. Historically, environmental conditions and the social and economic needs of the population made flood plains attractive places to build settlements, despite the risk of periodic flooding. As a result there is a large amount of existing development on flood plains in the United Kingdom, some of which is very old – dating from long before modern planning systems existed. Much of this development is from periods of rapid urban expansion during the 19th and early 20th centuries. Some was of an industrial nature and there are some areas which may not be particularly sensitive to flood damage.

CHAPTER 2

However, modern interior fittings and electrical systems are more prone to damage during a flood event, and occupiers of properties on a flood plain are likely to be less tolerant of periodic flooding than were previous generations. There is also pressure for additional development in existing urban areas, including those located within flood plains and low-lying areas. According to Crichton (2003) 10 per cent of all new houses constructed between 1990 and 1995 were built in flood plains.

The floods of 1953 are a constant reminder of the significant areas of the United Kingdom that are at risk from tidal flooding. The floods of the 1990s and early 2000s have led to a wider public appreciation that large numbers of properties are at risk of fluvial flooding, even where they have not been flooded for many years. It is also clear, from recent floods, that **properties outside traditional flood plains may still be vulnerable to non-fluvial types of flooding, such as groundwater flooding or overland flow.** Effective and rational assessment of flood risk is essential to avoid the problem of unnecessary blight of existing development areas, and to prevent inappropriate development in areas subject to significant levels of flood risk.

There is also growing evidence that the climate is changing, and will continue to change even if production of greenhouse gases is reduced. It is likely that the effects of climate change on the United Kingdom will result in rises in sea level and increases in the intensity and duration of rainfall events (Defra, 2003; Hassell *et al*, 2002). These are likely to increase the probability of flooding in vulnerable areas, with greater potential for resultant damage and economic loss.

2.1.2   Defining flood risk

The risk of a given flood affecting people and property needs to be assessed and, if appropriate, mitigated and managed. To be able to do this, the concept of flood risk needs to be defined.

A commonly used definition is that flood risk reflects the level of exposure to the flood hazard. It is therefore a combination of the probability of the flood hazard occurring and the magnitude of the potential consequences of such a flood (Box 2.1).

Box 2.1   *Flood risk*

Flood risk is a combination of the probability of the flood hazard occurring and the magnitude of the potential consequences of a flood.

Flood probability

The probability of a flood hazard can be described as the chance that it will happen in any one year (Section 2.1.3).

Consequences of flooding

The consequences of flooding will depend upon the nature of the flood hazard and the vulnerability of an area. The nature of the flood hazard affects the potential for the flood to cause damage, and will be influenced by factors such as:

- flood depth
- flood velocity
- rate of onset of flooding
- flood duration
- wave action effects
- water quality.

Box 2.1 *Flood risk (cont)*

> The vulnerability of the area flooded affects the potential for damage to be caused and will be influenced by factors such as:
>
> - the number of properties and/or size of area affected
> - the type of development (eg more damage would be caused during the flooding of a supermarket than during the flooding of a park)
> - the nature of the population at risk (eg elderly or infirm people are more likely to suffer during flooding)
> - the presence and reliability of mitigation measures to manage flood risk.
>
> The combined influence of these factors will determine flood risk at a site. An assessed high risk of flooding, implying the need for mitigation measures, could arise from a very severe flood event with a low probability or a much more probable, and therefore (on average) more frequent, flood event which causes less damage and disruption.

The use of a source-pathway-receptor model (Fleming, 2001) can be a useful way of visualising flood risk relationships (Figure 2.1). From the construction industry's perspective, it is obvious that any risk management measures must be limited to what can be safely controlled. This implies that most risk management approaches for development will concentrate primarily on the receptor (people, property, infrastructure) and, in some cases, on the pathway (catchment, land, watercourses and any obstructions to flow) as well.

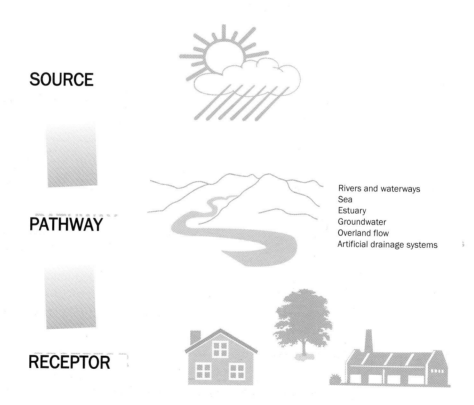

SOURCE

PATHWAY

Rivers and waterways
Sea
Estuary
Groundwater
Overland flow
Artificial drainage systems

RECEPTOR

Figure 2.1 *Source-pathway-receptor model for floods* (after Fleming, 2001)

In the wider context, a comprehensive assessment of flood risk should include consideration of not just the definition of flood risk given in Box 2.1, but also of the economic, social and environmental issues associated with flooding (Figure 2.2). The aim of flood risk assessment is to provide a rational and consistent approach to the decision-making process, allowing practical, sustainable actions and/or mitigation measures to be implemented where necessary.

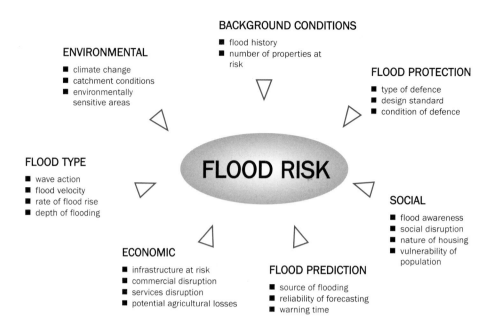

Figure 2.2 *Factors affecting flood risk* (after Fleming, 2001)

2.1.3 Probability of flood events

In general, floods that cause significant impacts on large numbers of people are relatively infrequent. **The timing of flood events is difficult to predict, as they occur as a result of specific combinations of environmental and meteorological factors. However, the probability that a particular magnitude of flood will occur sometime in the future can be estimated.**

It is important that the meaning and implications of flood probability, together with the inherent uncertainties involved with assessing it, are understood by all those involved in the consideration of flood risk.

Until recently it was common practice for flood studies to use the average period between events, expressed as a return period, to describe the probability of a flood event of given magnitude. For example, a flood with a long-term average recurrence interval of 100 years was called a 100 year return period flood. However, it is now generally considered that this concept may be misleading as, after a flood that is deemed to have had a return period of 100 years or more occurs, many may consider it most unlikely that such an event will occur again in their lifetime. The 1990s and early 2000s were a shock to many people in flood affected areas, when a succession of "long return period" (ie relatively infrequent) flood events occurred within a few years, or even months, of each other.

It is now considered that the expression of annual flood probability in terms of return periods should be avoided (Fleming, 2001). The preferred terminology used in this guide is the percentage probability of a flood of a given magnitude being equalled or exceeded in any year (see Box 2.2).

Box 2.2 *Expressions of annual flood probability*

Annual probability of flood event	Basis of expression	Expressed as a return period
2%	1-in-50 chance of being equalled or exceeded in any year	50 year flood
1%	1-in-100 chance of being equalled or exceeded in any year	100 year flood
0.5%	1-in-200 chance of being equalled or exceeded in any year	200 year flood

Annual flood probability should not be expressed in terms of a return period as this may be misleading.

If older studies use return period the annual flood probability as a percentage can be determined as 100/return period.

It is important to understand that even relatively low probability floods, considered over a long period of time, have a significant likelihood of occurring. The *Flood Estimation Handbook* (Institute of Hydrology, 1999) gives an equation to estimate the likelihood of a flood of given probability occurring during a specified period. For example, **a 1 per cent annual probability flood has a 22 per cent chance of occurring at least once in a 25 year period (the duration of a typical residential mortgage), and a 53 per cent chance of occurring at least once in a 75 year period (a typical human lifetime).**

In areas where flooding is caused by the combined effect of two or more mechanisms, the probability of flooding as a result of the coincidence of the various flooding mechanisms must be assessed. Such studies are referred to as joint probability assessments. Typical situations where a joint probability assessment may be required include tidal reaches of watercourses, where flooding may be caused by a number of combinations of tidal level and fluvial flow, and locations near the confluence of two watercourses. Joint probability problems are complex (Institute of Hydrology, 1999) and expert advice should be sought in such situations.

2.1.4   Perception of flood risk

While it is possible to estimate probabilities of flood events, it should be remembered that the way flood risk is perceived will be subjective. Fleming (2001) points out that before the 1990s the United Kingdom experienced around 30 years without significant flooding capturing the attention of the media and the public. However, the floods of 1998 and 2000 in England and Wales highlighted to many that their properties are at risk of periodic flooding... not a risk they had previously considered. One result of greater population mobility is that the average period of residential occupancy of a given property has significantly reduced compared to 50 years ago. As a result, local knowledge of previous flooding can become diluted, reducing the perceived flood risk to the level where it is no longer recognised by residents and landowners.

2.2   TYPES OF FLOODING

There is sometimes a presumption that managing flood risk is all about dealing with fluvial flooding caused by rivers, and this may be related to the very obvious common sense link between a swollen river and the risk of a site being inundated. However, recent studies have indicated that **a significant proportion of flood-related insurance claims within the United Kingdom are from non-fluvial flooding**. Crichton (2003) estimates that between 30 and 50 per cent of insurance claims following the autumn 2000 floods, arose from properties outside of the flood plains associated with rivers. A rational assessment of the potential for flooding to affect a development site, or for development to exacerbate flood risk elsewhere, requires that the full range of possible types of flooding be considered.

Box 2.3 lists the principal categories of flooding mechanisms that can affect development sites.

Box 2.3   *Categories of flood mechanisms*

Category	Mechanism
Fluvial flooding	Exceedence of the flow capacity of the channel of a river, stream or other natural watercourse, typically associated with heavy rainfall events. Excess water spills onto the flood plain
Coastal and tidal flooding	High tides, storm surges and wave action, often in combination
Estuarial flooding and watercourses affected by tidelocking	Often involving high tidal levels and high fluvial flows in combination
Groundwater flooding	Raised groundwater levels, typically following prolonged rain (may be slow to recede). High groundwater levels may result in increased overland flow flooding
Flooding from overland flow	Water flowing over the ground surface that has not reached a natural or artificial drainage channel. This can occur when intense rainfall exceeds the infiltration capacity of the ground, or when the ground is so highly saturated that it cannot accept any more water
Flooding from artificial drainage systems	Blockage or overloading of pipes, sewers, canals, and drainage channels or failure of pumping systems. Typically following heavy rain or as a result of high water levels in a receiving watercourse
Flooding from infrastructure failure	Structural, hydraulic or geotechnical failure of infrastructure that retains, transmits or controls the flow of water

These flooding mechanisms are described in the following sections.

2.2.1   Fluvial flooding

Flooding from rivers, streams and other inland natural watercourses is usually caused by prolonged or intense rainfall, generating high rates of runoff which overwhelm the capacity of the river or channel to transmit the water downstream (Box 2.4). Prolonged periods of high rainfall in the United Kingdom are typically associated with depressions moving in from the Atlantic, although short-term very intense rainfall can also lead to very high runoff rates. If significant rainfall occurs following a wet period, so that much of the catchment is already at (or close to) saturation, then very high rates and volumes of runoff can occur. Similarly, a highly urbanised catchment with large areas of impermeable surfaces (roofs, roads, car parks etc) can also generate high rates of runoff, which may be conveyed rapidly to watercourses by the drainage system.

Box 2.4   *Fluvial flooding*

During the autumn of 2000, as a result of an extended period of heavy rainfall, more than 10 000 properties were flooded in over 700 locations across England and Wales. An estimated 37 000 homes only narrowly avoided flooding,, and widespread disruption of road and rail links occurred due to flooding. Some places were subject to flooding up to five times during the autumn of 2000. It is estimated that the damage caused was in the order of £1 billion, and many people were displaced from their homes for several months.

Source: Environment Agency (2001)

Snowmelt and "rain on snow" events may also occur in the United Kingdom, and while these are less common than events caused by rainfall alone, they have resulted in some of the most significant flood events, eg the widespread flooding experienced in 1947.

If the flow generated exceeds the capacity of the channel of a watercourse then the excess water will spill onto any low-lying areas adjacent to or contiguous with the channel – this area is known as the flood plain (Figure 2.3).

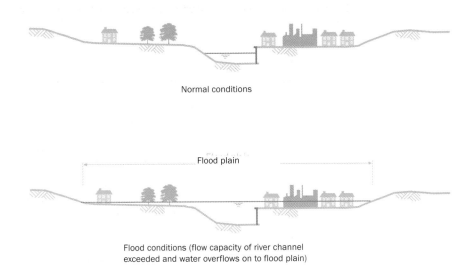

Normal conditions

Flood plain

Flood conditions (flow capacity of river channel exceeded and water overflows on to flood plain)

Figure 2.3   *The flood plain and fluvial flooding*

Flooding of flood plains is a natural phenomenon, although it may be influenced by man-made changes to catchment areas and watercourse systems. Such flooding plays an important role in moderating flood conditions within the watercourse system, by attenuating the highest peak flows. The excess water leaving the watercourse is temporarily stored on the flood plain and this reduces the peak of the flood wave. This means that peak flood flows downstream are lower than they would have been without the overflow onto the flood plain (Figure 2.4).

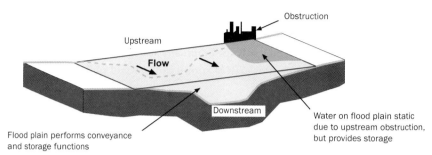

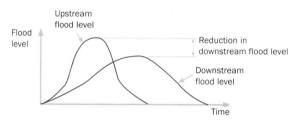

a) Undefended flood plain that provides flood storage

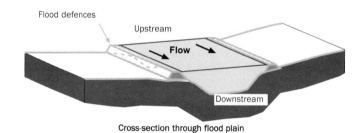

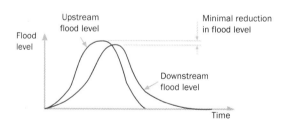

b) Flood plain with defence structures (limited flood storage)

Figure 2.4 *Effect of flood plain storage on downstream flows* (after Fleming, 2001)

Storage of water occurs across the whole flood plain. Some areas of flood plain can be purely storage areas (Figure 2.4a). In such washland areas water velocities are negligible but the water standing on the flood plain is retained, leading to reduced peak flows downstream. Storage of flood plain water also occurs in areas where water velocities are significant and flood water is conveyed downstream.

The extent of the flood plain is defined by the probability of the flood event. For example the flood plain associated with a 5 per cent annual probability event will generally be smaller in extent than the flood plain associated with floods of lower probability (such as a 1 per cent or 0.5 per cent probability flood), where the flood level will be higher, and the flooding more widespread. Information on the basis of any available mapping of the flood plain, and associated uncertainties, in a specific area can be obtained from the flood defence agency (FDA).

A distinction is sometimes made between the functional flood plain and the passive flood plain (DTLR, 2001):

> **Functional flood plains** are the unobstructed areas of the flood plain where water regularly flows in time of flood, ie where there are no effective defences against a flood (Figure 2.5a). Some urban areas fall within the active flood plain but, because of the obstructions due to built development, they are not regarded as fully functional.

> **Passive flood plains** are areas that are within the natural flood plain but are not now subject to frequent flooding, because of the presence of flood alleviation measures (Figure 2.5b). In the event of a flood greater than that for which the alleviation measures were designed, such a passive flood plain would still be at risk of flooding.

The above definitions of functional and passive flood plains are currently under review, but the FDA may be able to provide information on current definitions.

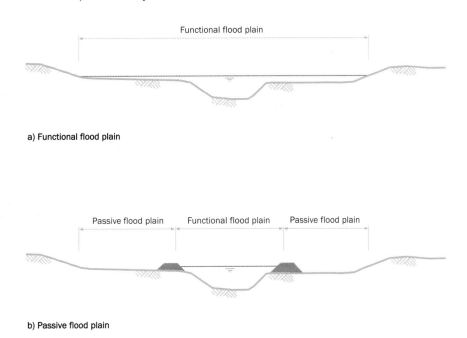

a) Functional flood plain

b) Passive flood plain

Figure 2.5   *Functional and passive flood plains*

2.2.2 Coastal flooding

Coastal flooding, caused by high tides and extreme weather conditions, has the potential to affect a large number of properties in the United Kingdom (Box 2.5).

Box 2.5 *Coastal flooding*

On 31 January 1953 widespread coastal flooding occurred along the east coast of England. The combination of a high spring tide, a deep atmospheric low over the North Sea and northerly gales, created a storm surge which breached the flood defences along the coast. The subsequent flooding led to the inundation of more than 24 500 houses and evacuation of some 30 000 people. The high depths (the old town of Harwich was flooded to a depth of 3.7 metres) and rapid onset of flooding caught many people unawares, trapping some in their homes, and causing significant damage to many properties. More than 300 people died.

Source: Environment Agency (2003a)

Coastal flooding is caused by extreme tidal conditions which can occur due to three main mechanisms and, most commonly, as a combination of two or more of these (Institute of Hydrology, 1999):

1   **High astronomical tide level:** cyclical variation in tide levels due to the gravitational effects of (mainly) the sun and moon. These effects lead to the twice-daily variation between high and low tide, and to the spring-neap tide cycle, which occurs approximately monthly, largely controlled by the phases of the moon.

2   **Surge:** an increase in water level above the astronomical tide level caused by low barometric pressure exacerbated by the wind acting on the surface of the sea.

3   **Wave action:** dependent on wind speed and direction, local topography and exposure, sometimes combined with oceanic swell waves.

Coastal flooding may occur over areas not protected by existing flood defences or due to overtopping or breaching of existing sea defences such as embankments or walls. While sea defences are present around much of the United Kingdom's at-risk coastline, the consequences of defence failure may be severe.

2.2.3 Estuarial flooding and watercourses affected by tidelocking

Flooding along estuaries may occur either under the influence of tidal factors or as a result of tidal influence in combination with fluvial flows (Figure 2.6). **In most cases the tidal flows will have the dominant effect on estuarial flood levels,** but fluvial flows can have a secondary contributory effect. Local conditions within an estuary can have a significant effect on flood levels. For example, the shape of an estuary channel can cause the high water level to increase as a tide moves up an estuary from the sea. Before the construction of modern flood alleviation measures (including the Thames Barrier), areas around London were affected (in 1928 and 1953) by severe flooding from the River Thames, caused by a combination of tidal (spring tides and storm surge) and river (high flows caused by runoff) influences.

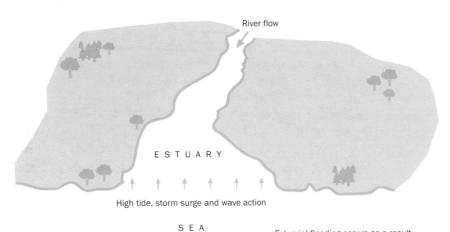

River flow

ESTUARY

High tide, storm surge and wave action

SEA

Estuarial flooding occurs as a result of the influence of the sea, possibly in combination with river flow

Figure 2.6 *Estuarial flooding*

A common problem in tidally-affected areas occurs where flood defences exist. Smaller watercourses must pass beneath the defences and their outfalls must be provided with flap valves to prevent the penetration of estuarial waters up the watercourse. These devices allow water to drain out of the watercourses at low tides but once the tide level rises above that in the watercourse, the water pressure will cause the gates to close, preventing ingress of sea water. Unless the watercourse is provided with a pumping station then the watercourse will be "tidelocked" and water will not be able to exit the watercourse until the level in the watercourse exceeds that of the tide (Figure 2.7). A combination of high tide and significant flows in the watercourse may lead to the build up of water in the watercourse and cause flooding, even if the estuary defences are not overtopped.

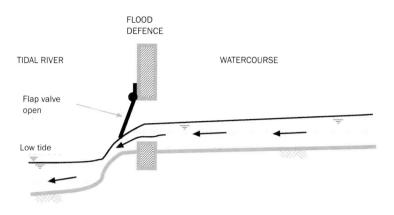

Low tide – free outflow from watercourse

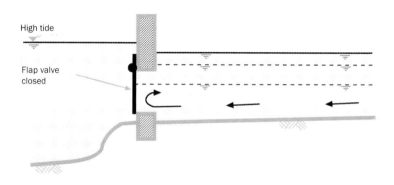

High tide – flap valve closes. No outflow leads to a build-up
of water levels in watercourse

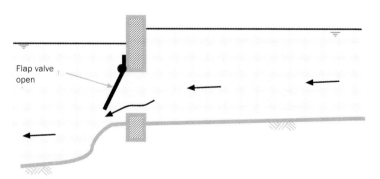

High tide – once watercourse level increases to above tide
level, outflow occurs

Figure 2.7   *Tidelocking of watercourses*

2.2.4 Groundwater flooding

Increased groundwater levels caused by prolonged periods of rainfall can result in flooding. **Groundwater may not be perceived to be a major factor contributing to flood risk but, in the winter of 2000/2001 more than 1000 homes and businesses in the United Kingdom were affected** (ODPM, 2002). Several parts of the country experienced groundwater flooding (Box 2.6), but the most severely affected were those areas underlain by the Chalk outcrop in south east England (Robinson *et al*, 2001).

Box 2.6   *Groundwater flooding*

During the winter of 2000–2001 groundwater flooding occurred in several areas underlain by the Chalk aquifer in Hampshire. In one location a winterbourne stream began to flow in an area previously lowered by flint and chalk excavation for railway construction in the 19th century. This local depression became a lake estimated to be 6 hectares in size and eventually overflowed into the village. Consequently the main road through the village was closed and several adjacent properties flooded. A new housing development of 14 houses in a low-lying area were flooded to a depth of more than 1 metre.

Groundwater flooding of new properties in a low-lying area

The flooding persisted for more than four months, and traffic on the main road through the village had to be controlled by traffic lights because of the flow of water down the road. The flooded properties in the new development were permanently abandoned.

Pictures from the village Millennium Book clearly show that the flooded field, where the properties were built, and the main road through the village flooded on several occasions during the 20th century. Groundwater flooding at this site was therefore not unprecedented, although the 2000–2001 flooding persisted for much longer than earlier events. Had the risk of groundwater flooding been adequately assessed during planning, the inappropriate development of an area at risk from groundwater flooding could have been avoided.

Generally, groundwater flooding may be a problem where developments are underlain by permeable soils or rocks (known as aquifers). Examples of aquifers in the United Kingdom include Chalk, Limestone and Sandstone. Aquifers often have an extensive capacity to receive and store water from rainfall, which results in rises in groundwater level. This storage means that in many cases heavy rainfall can be absorbed by aquifers without any resultant flooding. However, if above average rainfall persists for extended periods, groundwater levels may ultimately rise to ground level (Figure 2.8). This can cause seepage into basements, ponding of water in low-lying areas, and the re-emergence of normally dry groundwater springs and ephemeral watercourses (known as "winterbournes" in areas underlain by Chalk). Problems may result from the emergence of this water; groundwater flooding has resulted in the flooding of properties, fields and roads. Increased groundwater levels can also result in high levels of infiltration to sewers, soakaways and underground services, reducing their capacity to remove surface water runoff. High groundwater levels can also significantly reduce the capacity of SUDS systems to receive infiltration, and so result in increased overland flow.

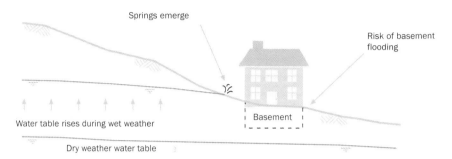

Figure 2.8 *Groundwater flooding*

Once groundwater flooding occurs, it may take a long time for groundwater levels to fall and flooding to abate, as the water stored in the aquifer drains slowly over weeks or months. This can increase the damage from groundwater flooding as more extensive water and damp penetration occurs during long inundations.

A key issue regarding groundwater flooding is that it may occur in areas outside flood plains associated with watercourses, and there may be no obvious visual clues that the site would be at risk of flooding if groundwater levels rose. This type of flooding can be very localised. This is because the geology of the underlying aquifers is a key controlling factor, and the existence of permeable fissures or joints, or variations in aquifer properties can result in groundwater emerging at the surface at very specific and localised points. These locations are often the locations of old springs or ephemeral streams. If these flow during only the very wettest periods, their presence may have become almost forgotten by the local population, and development may have occurred nearby, without regard for the possible flood risk.

In some parts of the country, particularly urban areas, groundwater levels may be rising as a result of reductions in groundwater abstractions during the latter part of the 20th century (Simpson *et al*, 1989; Wilkinson and Brassington, 1991). The risk of groundwater flooding may be increased where rising groundwater levels affect shallow water tables.

2.2.5 ## Overland flow flooding

Overland flow is water flowing over the ground surface that has not entered a natural drainage channel or artificial drainage system (other commonly used terms for this phenomenon are pluvial flooding or surface water runoff flooding). There are records of resulting flood damage in the East and West Midlands of England, the Isle of Wight and Somerset between the 1970s and 1990s (Boardman, 1995). Typically, **overland flow can cause localised flooding in natural valley bottoms as normally dry areas become covered in flowing water, and in natural low spots where the water may pond** (Figure 2.9). This flooding mechanism can occur almost anywhere, but is likely to be of particular concern in any topographical low spot, or where the pathway for runoff is restricted by terrain or man-made obstructions (Box 2.7).

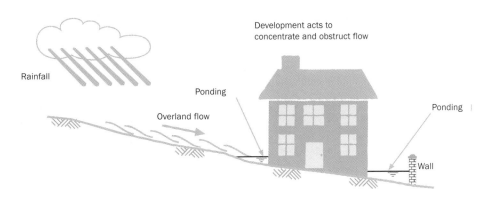

Figure 2.9 *Overland flow flooding*

Box 2.7 *Overland flow flooding*

During late June and early July 2003, heavy rainfall resulted in the rapid saturation of hillsides on the periphery of an urban area. Water began to run over the ground surface and was concentrated by walls and highway channels. In places the water overtopped the kerb lines and ran down through paths and gardens, flooding garages and causing problems with entry into buildings. These flows lasted for three days and a second incident occurred only weeks later.

Overland flow is caused when the intensity of rainfall exceeds the infiltration capacity of the surface onto which it falls (infiltration-excess overland flow) or when, during prolonged periods of wet weather, the soil is so saturated such that it cannot accept any more water (saturation-excess overland flow). Developments that include significant impermeable surfaces, such as roads, car parks and roofs, may increase the occurrence of overland flow. Overland flow will tend to occur for a similar period of time as the rainfall event that causes it. However, the flood water may remain for some time after accumulating at the surface in low areas with no significant outlet. This type of flow may occur as sheet flow or, on erodible surfaces, may form rills and gulleys during storm events. Overland flow can also result in so-called "muddy floods" where soil and stones are washed onto roads and into properties.

Overland flow may also occur where water that is flowing through the soil or rock below ground level returns to the surface, where the soil is saturated further down the slope (return flow). This type of overland flow is a form of shallow groundwater flooding and typically occurs at the base of slopes, where the surface gradient changes. This will be for a longer duration than the excess overland flow types as it is fed by water stored in, and running through, the soil from upslope, and may be supplemented by regional groundwater flooding (Section 2.2.4).

2.2.6 Flooding from artificial drainage systems

Many artificial drainage systems, such as pipes, land drains, sewers, and drainage channels (eg ditches and culverts), exist to manage runoff and effluent from developments. During heavy rainfall, flooding from artificial drainage systems may occur if the rainfall event exceeds the capacity of the drainage system (Box 2.8), or if the system becomes blocked by debris or sediment. This will also occur if the system surcharges due to a high water level in the receiving watercourse (Figure 2.10). **Flooding results if water overflows from the drainage system, or if water is unable to enter a drainage system that is blocked or has inadequate capacity.** Problems sometimes occur where existing land drainage systems have become disrupted by development or construction work, and have not been tied into the development drainage strategy. During heavy rainfall these drains may discharge water as artificial springs, resulting in flooding.

Box 2.8 *Flooding from artificial drainage system*

> On 30 July 2002 an intense rainfall event led to the flooding of areas in and around Glasgow which led to flows in excess of the capacity of urban watercourses and the sewer system.
>
> Flooding from sewers caused disruption to road and rail links, and led to the flooding of more than 500 properties.

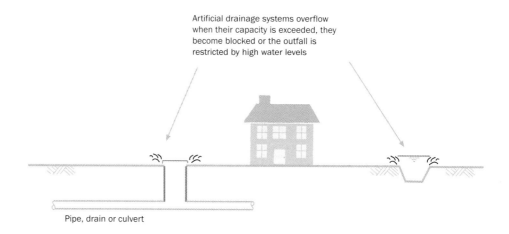

Artificial drainage systems overflow when their capacity is exceeded, they become blocked or the outfall is restricted by high water levels

Pipe, drain or culvert

Figure 2.10 *Flooding from artificial drainage systems*

Flooding from artificial drainage systems can occur more frequently than from other sources as many of these systems were designed to a lower standard than that required for new development. For example, drainage ditches created to improve agricultural productivity are unlikely to have been designed to contain flows greater than the 10 per cent annual probability of exceedence flow (ADAS, 1984).

Flooding from artificial drainage systems may occur during events that are below the design capacity of the system if the system capacity is temporarily reduced due to blockage by debris (Section 2.2.7). This can be a particular problem with underground drains or sewers, since the location of the blockage may not be easy to identify or to clear. Flooding may also result if a pumping station fails (Section 2.2.7). Causes of flooding from sewers are summarised in Box 2.9. Infiltration of groundwater into sewer systems may also reduce their capacity to receive and transmit runoff.

Box 2.9   *Common causes of flooding from sewers* (from May *et al*, 1998)

- inadequate flow capacity in public sewers
- random blockages in pipes and intercepting traps
- recurring blockages (due to characteristics of sewerage systems)
- inability of drainage flows from basements to enter public sewers
- pumping station failures
- burst rising mains
- high watercourse or tide levels causing inflows to sewers
- siltation (due to flat sewer gradients or sewer features)
- build-up of fats and greases
- sewer collapses.

Flooding from foul or combined foul and surface water sewer systems may be particularly unpleasant as flood waters are contaminated with sewage, with the resultant health risks. Flood water can sometimes enter directly into properties via the foul drainage system (through toilets etc). Fluvial flooding can also be contaminated with sewage as a result of combined sewer overflows or where there is a connection between the surface and foul drainage systems.

Flooding can also occur from canals and reservoirs. Flooding from reservoirs is rare, and is usually due to failure of the impounding structure (see Section 2.2.7). Hughes *et al* (2000) describe a risk management approach to dealing with the hazard posed by dams and reservoirs in the United Kingdom. Reservoirs generally have a positive impact in flood risk terms, as they attenuate runoff.

2.2.7   Flooding from infrastructure failure

Where infrastructure exists that retains, transmits or controls the flow of water, flooding may result if there is a structural, hydraulic, geotechnical, mechanical or operational failure (Figure 2.11). The risk of this mechanism of flooding is associated with three main categories of infrastructure:

- failure of infrastructure designed to store or carry water (eg dam break, canal leak, water mains burst)

- failure of infrastructure designed to protect an area from flooding (eg flood defence breach (Box 2.10), flap valve failure, penstock failure, pumping station failure)

- blockage of a pipe, bridge or culvert.

Because of the sudden onset of the flooding from these mechanisms, the impacts can be severe.

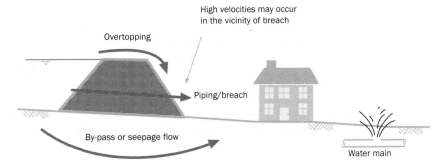

Figure 2.11 *Flooding from infrastructure failure*

Box 2.10 *Case history – flooding due to infrastructure failure*

During the major flood event of autumn 2000 high tide and river flow conditions led to the failure of a flood defence embankment protecting a village located approximately 1 kilometre away. Floodwater flowed over low-lying farmland and inundated much of the village. A further breach of the flood defence subsequently occurred immediately downstream of the village exacerbating the problem.

The flood had a major impact on the village, with properties inundated up to ceiling level in the worst cases. This resulted in general evacuation with many residents living in temporary accommodation for several months while awaiting completion of lengthy repairs. Some properties remained under water for up to two weeks, despite the best efforts by the Environment Agency and emergency services. Extensive works have now been undertaken to reinforce the flood defence and the breach risk is now much reduced, although not removed.

There is an increased risk of infrastructure failure during a flood event when the conditions put physical pressure on the operation of systems, and the high rates of flow mean that flooding will occur unless problems are rectified quickly. Flood defence infrastructure is particularly likely to fail under such conditions. For example, sea defences may fail as a result of damage due to overtopping by waves.

So called "sunny-day" or "blue sky" floods may also occur due to failure under normal hydrological conditions. For example, burst water mains may cause flooding of adjacent basements, or of low-lying properties, even during dry weather.

2.3 THE IMPACT OF CLIMATE CHANGE ON FLOOD RISK

Increasing global temperatures and changing weather patterns indicate that human-induced climate change is a reality. **Climate change has important implications for the assessment of flood risk** and for the design of mitigation measures such as flood defences.

The United Kingdom Climate Impacts Programme (UKCIP) is assessing the implications of climate change on the United Kingdom and, as part of this, the impacts on flood risk are being assessed. There is considerable uncertainty associated with the results, but current best practice (DTLR, 2001; Defra, 2003) is to make an allowance for climate change impacts, based on the latest predictions, when carrying out flood risk assessments.

It is predicted that rises in sea levels are likely to result in increased risk of coastal flooding, and may require changes to existing sea defences.

It is predicted that the United Kingdom will experience hotter summers and warmer, wetter, winters. Increases in the frequency and severity of storms are also predicted. The increased runoff from more intense rainfall may result in more flashy flood conditions and may result in increased flooding due to overland flow, and from artificial drainage systems as well as from watercourses. Wetter winters may result in increased groundwater levels and saturated ground conditions, leading to increased watercourse flows, greater runoff and overland flow from saturated soils and increased risk of groundwater flooding.

The scenarios published in 2002 suggest that winter daily precipitation may increase by 5 to 20 per cent by 2080, with autumn rainfall being up to 20 per cent lower (Hulme *et al*, 2002). The simulations suggest a higher flood probability in winter, but a reduction of flooding in spring and summer (Hawkes *et al*, 2002). The simulations indicate a continued increase in sea levels around the United Kingdom at rates of several millimetres per year.

It is uncertain what the impact of climate change will be on short duration rainfall events typically associated with summer storms. These storms can cause localised flooding, particularly in developed areas. Any increase in the rainfall intensity, or the frequency of such storms, will increase the incidence of local flooding.

Changes in climate in the United Kingdom imply that flood defences designed in the past to provide a specific standard of protection will not provide that standard in the future. The potential for increased rates of runoff may also affect the performance of existing infrastructure such as sewers, canals, reservoirs etc, resulting in increased flood risk. The impact of climate change on existing flood defences in Scotland was assessed by Price and McInally (2001) who estimated that sea defence levels designed to the 1 per cent annual probability standard in 1990 would provide a lesser standard of protection of only 5 to 10 per cent annual probability by 2050. With regard to fluvial flood defence standards, they estimated that the 1990, 1 per cent flood defence standard would be equivalent to approximately 1.5 per cent by 2050 and around 2 per cent by 2080.

Defra (2003) has produced suggested allowances to be used to assess the potential impact of climate change when planning flood alleviation schemes for fluvial and coastal flooding (Table 2.1). Allowances for climate change should also be made when assessing flood risk associated with other types of flooding.

Table 2.1 *Defra recommendations for climate change allowances for fluvial and coastal flooding* (May 2003)

Parameter	Recommendation	Comment
Mean and extreme sea level	4, 5 or 6 mm/year for different regions	Extreme levels should be reviewed if higher extreme values, especially around the Thames Estuary, are supported by future modelling
High and extreme river flow	Test sensitivity to additional 20 per cent in peak flow or volume over 50 years	Further research currently in progress
High and extreme wind speeds	Test sensitivity to 10 per cent increase in offshore wind speeds and wave heights by 2080 (and 5 per cent increase in wave periods)	Needs to be considered in relation to depth limited conditions inshore

Future climate change modelling may produce new predictions of the impact on flood risk in the future. **Any flood risk assessment should use the most up-to-date guidance available, and arrangements for including allowances for climate change impacts should be agreed with the FDA** (Box 5.3).

3. Developments and flooding

Developments that are designed without regard to flood risk may endanger lives, damage property, cause significant disruption to the wider community, damage the environment, be difficult to insure and require additional expense on remedial works. Such developments are, therefore, not sustainable.

To ensure that flood risk is assessed in an informed context it is essential that the construction industry considers the ways in which a development can be affected by flooding, and how the presence of a development may itself change flood risk elsewhere. This chapter presents the background to these issues.

3.1 TYPES OF DEVELOPMENT

A variety of development types, not just residential or commercial property, may be vulnerable to flood damage. Development types where flood risk needs to be considered include:

- residential property – houses, flats, apartments, caravans, mobile homes etc
- business premises – offices, shops, factories, distribution facilities, quarries etc
- public facilities – hospitals, civic buildings, parks, playing fields, habitat enhancement schemes, waste disposal sites etc
- transport links – roads, railways, cycleways, waterways etc
- infrastructure – bridges, tunnels, cuttings, culverts etc
- Service infrastructure – pumping stations, substations, treatment works, routing centres for water, gas, electric, communication utilities etc.

3.2 THE IMPACT OF FLOODING ON DEVELOPMENT

Flooding may affect developments in several ways. The direct physical impacts of a flood are fairly obvious and often are among the first things considered. However, any consideration of flood impacts should recognise, in addition to the physical impacts, the potential economic, social, environmental, health, safety and welfare impacts.

3.2.1 Physical impacts

Flooding can cause severe damage to properties. Flood water may enter properties by a variety of routes (Figure 3.1) including (ODPM, 2002):

- around closed doors
- through airbricks
- through windows (if water levels are sufficiently high)
- via backflow through overloaded sewers discharging into the property through toilets and sinks
- by seepage through external and party walls
- by seepage through the ground and into basements or up through the ground floor
- around cable services through external walls.

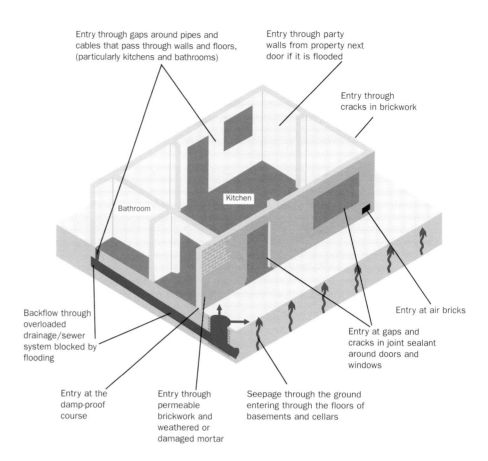

Entry through gaps around pipes and cables that pass through walls and floors, (particularly kitchens and bathrooms)

Entry through party walls from property next door if it is flooded

Entry through cracks in brickwork

Kitchen

Bathroom

Entry at air bricks

Backflow through overloaded drainage/sewer system blocked by flooding

Entry at gaps and cracks in joint sealant around doors and windows

Entry at the damp-proof course

Entry through permeable brickwork and weathered or damaged mortar

Seepage through the ground entering through the floors of basements and cellars

Figure 3.1 *Flood water penetration into a residential property* (adapted from ODPM, 2002)

Flooding can affect buildings in a variety of ways, including damage due to water penetration, impact of debris, pressure difference, buoyancy, sediment deposition and erosion (Kohli and Hager, 2001). Key factors in the amount of damage caused by flooding are listed in Box 2.1. The degree of flood warning received by those whose properties are flooded can have a significant impact on the level of damage that occurs to contents.

Table 3.1 indicates types of damage associated with various depths of flood water.

Table 3.1 *Flood damage for a typical residential property* (after ODPM, 2002)

Depth of flood water	Damage to the building	Damage to services and fittings	Damage to personal possessions
Below ground floor level	Minimal damage to the main building Flood water may enter basements, cellars and voids under floors Possible erosion beneath foundations	Damage to electrical sockets and other services in basements and cellars	Carpets in basements and cellars may need to be replaced Possessions and furniture in basements and cellars damaged
Up to half a metre above ground floor level	Damage to internal finishes, such as wall coverings and plaster linings. Wall coverings and linings may need to be stripped to allow walls to dry Floors and walls will become saturated and will require cleaning and drying out Damp problems may result	Chipboard flooring likely to require replacement Damage to internal and external doors and skirting boards Damage to downstairs electricity meter and consumer unit (fuse box) Damage to gas meters, low level boilers and telephone services	Carpets and floor coverings may need to be replaced Chipboard kitchen units are likely to require replacement Washing machines, free standing cookers, fridges and freezers may need to be replaced Damage to sofas, other furniture, and electrical goods Damage to small personal possessions, such as books, audio cassettes, videos and photographs Food in lower kitchen cupboards may be contaminated
More than half a metre above ground floor level	Increased damage to walls Possible structural damage	Damage to higher units, electrical services and appliances	Damage to possessions on higher shelves

Modern housing, if inappropriately designed, may be more susceptible to flood damage than older housing because many modern construction methods (eg chipboard floors, dry wall plasterboard, cavity insulation etc) are less resilient to flood damage. **The physical effects of flooding on developments do not disappear with the flood water and can have significant long-term impacts.** At the end of summer 2001 several thousand homes and businesses were still dealing with the effects of the flood events of autumn 2000 (ODPM, 2002).

Developments that do not consist of discrete properties (such as roads, service infrastructure etc) may be affected in different ways. Flooding may cause disruption of the services that such developments provide both during the flood event itself, for example through the severing of transport routes, and afterwards, as the clean-up operation may take a considerable amount of time. Bridges and other structures within the main flow area of the watercourse may be damaged due to impact loadings by debris carried along by the flood water, while high water velocities can also cause damage (eg due to scour). The damage and disruption from deposition of sediment and debris may also be a significant issue. Water penetration may be an issue affecting electrical or electronic controls.

3.2.2 Economic impacts

The economic costs of flooding can arise from direct and indirect damage (Table 3.2).

Table 3.2   *Direct and indirect economic damages due to flooding* (after Egli, 2002)

Effect on	Direct damage	Indirect damage
Housing	Damage to property Loss of furniture and assets	Expenditure for re-housing Expenditure for cleaning up
Public services and networks	Loss of property Loss of equipment	Expenditure for cleaning up Expenditure for organising rescue and substituting services
Crafts, trade, industry	Loss of materials, tools, stock	Expenditure for cleaning up Expenditure for moving Loss of business
Cultural heritage, environment	Damage to cultural heritage	Expenditure for restoration work
Local economy		Reduction in business income, value of property

The costs of flooding are increasing due to the increasing amount of electrical and electronic equipment within developments (ABI, 2002a). The ABI estimate that a depth of inundation of half a metre within a modern semi-detached house will result in an average cost of £15 000 to repair the building and £9,000 to replace damaged belongings (ODPM, 2002). Flooding by seawater may cause additional damage due to corrosion problems, which may increase flood damage repair costs by around 10 per cent (ODPM, 2002). There may also be additional costs associated with temporary accommodation during the period of repairs, which could last for several months. Comprehensive guidance on assessing the economic effects of flooding has been produced by Middlesex University Flood Hazard Research Centre, although the latest guidance is currently available only in draft form (Penning-Rowsell *et al*, 2003).

Social impacts

Flooding of developments can cause significant social impacts to those people living in or using the affected development, and also to the wider community around the development. The social impacts of flooding can include:

- psychological effects and stress on those affected by, or at risk of, flooding
- loss of personal possessions and items of sentimental importance, including pets
- housing loss and inconvenience of living in temporary accommodation
- disruption to key infrastructure and transport routes
- disruption to medical and other emergency services
- disruption to socio-economic activity, including loss of business
- potential barrier to redevelopment of brownfield urban sites
- loss of property value.

The impact on people as a result of the stress and trauma of being flooded, or even being under the threat of flooding, can be immense and should not be underestimated. These issues are discussed in Section 3.2.4.

The social impacts caused by flooding of developments may be exacerbated by the changing stance of the United Kingdom insurance industry to properties at risk of flooding. **Insurance companies are not obliged to provide flood insurance, and it is possible that insurance cover will not be available on all properties in flood risk areas**. The *ABI Statement of Principles on the Provision of Flooding Insurance* (ABI, 2002a) highlighted that, after 1 January 2003, the continuance of existing flood insurance cover would depend on the degree of flood risk associated with a property, as summarised in Table 3.3.

Table 3.3 *Summary of ABI approach to the provision of flooding insurance* (after ABI, 2002a)

Situation	Flooding insurance situation
Area currently defended to Defra minimum standard	Flood cover will be a standard feature of household and small business policies, but premiums will reflect different levels of risk
High risk areas where improved defences are planned by 2007	Flood cover will continue for domestic properties and small businesses. Consideration will be given to continuing to provide cover where a small business is sold. Premiums and terms will reflect the risk
High risk areas where no improvements in defences are planned	No guarantee that flood cover will continue to be provided, but risks will be considered on a case-by-case basis

The ABI guidance on insurance issues relating to flood risk (ABI, 2002b) indicates that the minimum standard of protection which would enable insurers to offer cover at normal terms for residential properties is 0.5 per cent or better up to the year 2050, after taking climate change into account.

Table 3.3 applies only to existing properties. The ABI guidance (ABI, 2002b) indicates that insurers believe that development in areas of high flood risk should be curtailed except in exceptional circumstances.

It should be noted that these insurance industry principles are subject to annual review, and implementation of these principles depends in part on the full application of the relevant planning policy guidance within the planning process (ABI, 2002a).

3.2.4 Health, safety and welfare impacts

The potential health impacts of flooding are summarised in Table 3.4. Direct impacts are caused by the flood waters themselves, while indirect impacts are caused by the damage to other systems caused by the flood. Effects may be acute (short-lived) or chronic (long-lasting). Comprehensive details of health issues related to flooding can be found in WHO (2002).

Table 3.4 *Health effects of flooding (after WHO, 2002)*

Effects	Causes
Direct effects	
Drowning, injuries from impacts and falls	Exposure to deep and/or flowing flood water, lack of adequate warning; fast flowing water carrying debris
Respiratory diseases, shock, hypothermia, cardiac arrest	Contact with flood waters
Wound infections, dermatitis, conjunctivitis, gastrointestinal illnesses, ear/nose/throat infections, possible serious waterborne diseases	Contact with polluted flood waters, exposure to damp conditions
Physical and emotional stress	Disturbance due to injury, loss of property, evacuation or perception of risk of flooding
Indirect effects	
Possible waterborne infections, dermatitis and conjunctivitis	Damage to water supply and sewerage systems, inadequate or contaminated supply of water
Food shortage, disruption of emergency response	Disruption to transport systems
Acute or chronic effects of chemical pollution	Leaks/overflows/releases from vehicles, storage tanks, or waste sites
Health and social care problems	Disruption or overloading of healthcare, community and social care systems

Immediate impacts

The obvious health and safety impacts relating to flooding are drowning or physical injury due to being swept away by flood waters. In 1953, during the floods along the east coast of England, 307 people died. As recently as Easter 1998 five people lost their lives directly or indirectly as a result of floods in the English Midlands (Bye and Horner, 1998).

It should be recognised that, in small urban catchments or where watercourses are "flashy" (ie have a very rapid response to rainfall), flood waters can rise very quickly. The depth and velocity of the flood water can be dangerous to people who are forced to wade through water to seek safety. Flood water may hide other hazards for wading pedestrians, such as manhole openings where the covers have been lifted by flood flows. Flood waters can wash vehicles and buildings away, with the potential for fatalities. Flooding can also occur very suddenly if defences are overtopped or breached. Guidance is available (HR Wallingford, 2003a) on the hazards to life associated with various depths and velocities of flood water.

Long-term impacts

In addition to the immediate impact of flooding, flood events can cause long-term impacts on people affected by floods, due to chronic illnesses and stress. Stress suffered by flood victims is often worse where the flooding is relatively frequent, or where sewage contamination has occurred. To be flooded out of your home, workplace or business, perhaps with very little warning, coupled with the loss of personal possessions or business assets, is probably one of the most traumatic events many people are likely to face during their lives. The distress is often compounded by the protracted clean-up and restoration process that has to follow.

Being caught in a flood event can be a terrifying experience. People affected by flooding may experience psychological effects following the stress of flooding. Subsequently repeated stress may be experienced after the flood caused by anxiety when periods of rainfall occur.

Flood water can be contaminated by sewage and other pollutants such as chemicals from residential garages or commercial properties that may have spilled into flood water. It can also leave behind sediments containing pollutants, and mould can grow in the damp conditions following flooding. This can lead to new health problems and can exacerbate existing health conditions in people living and working in flood affected areas.

The health and social effects of the June 2000 floods in north east England were reviewed by Tapsell *et al*, (2002) who state that a large number of health effects were reported, primarily related to the trauma of the flooding and then living in a damp and dirty environment.

3.2.5   Environmental impacts

Significant environmental effects caused by flooding on development sites can include soil erosion and damage to vegetation as well as the water quality and pollution effects which may be caused by bacteria and pollutants within flood water (Section 3.2.4).

However, incorporation of flood mitigation measures into the design of developments can have significant benefits to the environment of the development site and surrounding areas. The use of Sustainable Drainage Systems (SUDS) and retention of green space within flood plain areas can provide opportunity for biodiversity, habitat improvement and amenity space within development sites. Replacement of existing culverts with open watercourses can reduce flood risk and provide environmental benefit. Managed realignment of coastal areas may be undertaken as part of development site proposals to provide an opportunity for enhancement of the coastal area.

3.3   THE IMPACT OF DEVELOPMENT ON FLOOD RISK

3.3.1   Increases in the potential for flood damage

Development may increase flood risk if new buildings and/or infrastructure are sited in areas at risk of flooding (Box 3.1). Such a development will lead to a direct increase in the vulnerability of the area to flooding, as the potential for damage caused during a flood event will typically be much greater than before the development.

Box 3.1   *Case history – increase in the potential for flood damage*

> A residential development was constructed on the site of a disused sawmill which had used the flow from a small river. Although the site was known to be located within the flood plain, planning permission was granted for the development as the local planning authority was keen for the site to be redeveloped. Within 18 months of the completion of construction of the development the site was flooded to a depth of 0.3 m, causing significant damage to the new properties.

3.3.2 Changes in runoff

Developments that contain significant areas of impermeable surfaces (roofs, roads, hardstanding etc) may increase the flood hazard in other areas by increasing the rate and volume of runoff (Box 3.2). The impact of development on the runoff regime of an area can be summarised as (Environment Agency, 1999a):

- increased runoff from reduced-permeability surfaces

- decreased baseflow because of reduced recharge of groundwater

- decreased times to peak flow, changing the timing of runoff from the catchment and making the catchment more sensitive to short duration storms

- changes in critical season – rural catchments tend to flood after long winter storms while urban sites tend to be more at risk from short, heavy, storms which tend to occur in summer.

Box 3.2 *Increase in runoff*

This example shows a block of flats surrounded by impermeable road and car park areas. This development replaced an existing house with extensive gardens, increasing the amount of impermeable area within the plot of land.

The problem of flood risk being increased by changes in runoff patterns caused by development is increasingly recognised as a major issue. The use of Sustainable Drainage Systems (SUDS) is widely promoted as a means of reducing and attenuating runoff from development sites (Appendix A3.3.11) and, used appropriately, can be an important part of development drainage design (Martin *et al*, 2001).

3.3.3 Changes in flood risk upstream

Development, such as the construction of flood defences and watercourse crossings, can restrict the capacity of the watercourse and flood plain system. Where this occurs, water levels upstream will increase (Box 3.3). Similar effects can occur if a development disrupts artificial drainage systems, such as land drains. This increases the flood hazard adjacent to, and upstream of, the development site by increasing the potential level of flooding above that which would occur under existing conditions. The increase in water levels caused by a development will typically be greatest at the development itself, but will persist for some distance upstream.

Box 3.3   *Case history – change in flood risk upstream*

An extension to a sports facility was constructed in a shallow valley. A small stream was culverted for a distance of some 70 m under the new building. The size of the culvert was based on the size of an existing road culvert immediately downstream.

A screen was provided at the entrance to the culvert. The propensity for the screen to block with debris was overlooked. During a relatively small flood event one night, debris accumulated on the screen causing the upstream water level to rise. Water flowed out of the channel, causing flooding upstream of the culvert and of the sports building.

This example illustrates that culverting a stream under a building is inadvisable, and should be adopted only if there is no other alternative approach. Even where a culvert is large enough to carry the design flood flow, if the culvert or screen becomes blocked flooding can occur at relatively low flows.

The increase in upstream flood level in the watercourse channel and/or flood plain due to bridges and culverts is often referred to as "afflux". **Inappropriate development in the flood plain can also add to flood risk by providing obstructions to the flow,** which can lead to the accumulation of debris. This can block areas of flow, causing additional restriction and a further increase in upstream water levels.

3.3.4 Changes in flood risk downstream

In addition to increasing rates of runoff (Section 3.3.2), **development can cause an increase in flood risk downstream of the site if it leads to a decrease in the volume available for flood storage.** Compensatory flood plain storage may therefore be required (Box 3.4, Appendix A3.3.10). As discussed in Section 2.2.1, flood plain storage has a significant influence on downstream flood flows and, if this storage is reduced, flood risk downstream can be increased. As an example of the importance of flood plain storage, McCartney and Naden (1995) estimated that the removal of flood plain storage on the River Severn at Montford would cause up to a 24 per cent increase in flood flow.

Box 3.4   *Case history – compensatory flood plain storage*

A motorway was proposed which crossed the channel and flood plain of a main river. In addition to ensuring that the new road would not cause an increase in upstream flood risk, works were required to compensate for the volume of storage which would otherwise be lost due to the new road embankment. This required regrading of a large area of land outside the motorway corridor.

There is a general presumption that any development that might be allowed in the flood plain should not result in a net loss of flood storage volume. This generally applies to even the smallest development, as it is usually the potential cumulative loss of storage of a series of developments in the flood plain, rather than the effect of a single development, that is of concern. Storage of materials in the flood plain may also increase flood risk downstream as these materials may be carried off during a flood and may block bridges/culverts downstream.

3.3.5 Environmental impacts

Low-lying areas at risk of flooding or subject to seasonal waterlogging often comprise important environmental assets. Examples of such areas include Romney Marsh and the Somerset Levels. Such areas are often sensitive to change and the loss of natural wetland, coastal saltmarsh and water meadow areas – due to flood defences and land drainage improvement works – has led to a reduction in the bio-diversity of habitats within the United Kingdom.

Flood plains provide important ecological resources, including (Thomas, 1995):

- high biological productivity of flood plain and wetland vegetation

- natural genetic diversity

- breeding and feeding grounds for fish and wildlife

- waterfowl habitat

- habitat for rare and endangered species.

Flood plain areas are part of the river corridor habitat and form important linear landscape features along which wildlife can live and move (Environment Agency, 1999a).

Any disturbance to flood plain areas may have a detrimental impact on the environment through direct loss of habitat, or through changes to the water and sediment balance of the system. This will be especially important if the existing flood plain area forms a natural wetland or other habitat associated with intermittent inundation by flood water, or if the habitat is a site of nature conservation.

River/flood plain environments can also provide additional opportunities for other uses, such as navigation and recreation, can provide access routes between town and country and can have aesthetic value (Environment Agency, 1999a). Changes to the area of available flood plain and/or flood regime of a watercourse due to development may affect these functions.

Part B

FLOOD RISK ASSESSMENT

Part

B

4 Flood risk assessment within the planning process

4.1 INTRODUCTION

Planning policies and procedures across the United Kingdom are the mechanism by which development and the use of land is regulated, with the aim of promoting sustainable development. Flood risk is an important factor to be considered by planning authorities when preparing development plans and, where it is relevant, it is a "material consideration" to be taken into account by local planning authorities (LPAs) when determining planning applications.

The planning process requires an assessment to be made of any flood risks related to proposed developments. This primarily involves two key issues (see Chapter 3):

- whether the development itself would be at risk of being flooded

- whether the development would increase the risk of flooding elsewhere.

This is the essence of the flood risk assessment (FRA) process. The outcome of the FRA will be dependent on a variety of factors, including the location of the development and its proposed nature and use. The FRA process should assess risks associated with all types of flooding (such as groundwater and overland flow etc), not just fluvial or coastal flooding.

This chapter briefly outlines the principles used within the planning system to assess flood risk, and outlines the responsibilities of developers and other key parties within the planning system. This chapter describes the common elements of planning for flood risk management across the United Kingdom. Specific aspects of planning policies for England, Wales, Scotland and Northern Ireland are outlined in Appendices A1 to A4.

4.2 FLOOD RISK AND PLANNING

Planning systems in England, Wales, Scotland and Northern Ireland vary in detail because of differing legislation and local government arrangements. However, in principle, the approach to the control of development where flood risk is an issue is the same in each country. The principles underlying the management of flood risk are described below.

The planning process encourages sustainable development and requires the precautionary principle to be adhered to when making decisions based on estimates of present and future flood risks (Box 4.1).

Box 4.1 *Sustainable development and the precautionary principle*

In this context, **sustainable development** means development which meets the needs of the present without compromising the ability of future generations to meet their own needs. This can be achieved by, for example, directing development away from areas identified as being at high risk of flooding, preferably to areas where there is little or no such risk.

The **precautionary principle** states that lack of full scientific certainty shall not be used as a reason for postponing cost-effective measures to avoid or manage flood risk. In practice this means that the best currently available information should be used in assessments, even where uncertainty remains, but should be applied in a cautious manner to ensure that safe and sustainable outcomes are achieved.

The need for the application of the precautionary principle arises from the uncertainties inherent in flood risk assessment and mapping (Section 4.2.1). Even if a development lies outside the mapped indicative flood plain this does not necessarily mean there is no flood risk associated with the site. Flooding could emanate, for example, from groundwater or overland flow (see Section 2.2). Flooding could also occur in extreme flood events more severe than that defining the extent of the indicative flood plain. It should also be appreciated that the extent of the flood plain often cannot be accurately defined, particularly in flat lowland areas. The lines drawn on maps to define flood risk zones must therefore be used for guidance only, and not as definitive indicators of flood risk.

4.2.1 The sequential test and definitions of flood risk zones

The mechanism by which the aims of the planning process are achieved is the use of the sequential test, which promotes a risk-based approach to the assessment of whether a particular type of development is acceptable in an area subject to a given level of flood risk. In practice, the sequential test is applied through the use of flood risk zoning guidance, where the type of development that is permitted is controlled by the assessed level of flood risk. The precise details of the risk levels and associated development types for each zone may vary to some degree between guidance produced by different bodies. Nevertheless, all such guidance should ensure that **sensitive, critical or vulnerable developments are not located in areas at significant risk of flooding, unless there is compelling justification for doing so, and then only if the development design takes all flood risk issues into account.**

In England, Scotland and Wales, separate planning policy guidance documents relating to flood risk have been issued. In these documents, flood risk zones have been defined on the basis of the sequential test (Table 4.1). An equivalent document for Northern Ireland is expected during 2004. In each country, the planning response to flood risk associated with a development proposal will be based on the version of these planning policy guidance documents current at the time of the proposal. Further details of the guidance current in March 2004 for each country are given in Appendices A1 to A4.

Table 4.1 *National planning policies on development and flooding*

UK Country	National planning policy on development and flooding	Nomenclature for flood risk zones
England	PPG25: Development and Flood Risk, July 2001 (DTLR, 2001)	Zones 1, 2, 3a, 3b, 3c Zone 1: little or no risk Zone 2: low to medium risk Zone 3a: high risk – developed areas Zone 3b: high risk – undeveloped and sparsely developed areas Zone 3c: functional flood plains
Scotland	SPP7: Planning and Flooding, February 2004 (Scottish Executive, 2004)	Zones 1, 2, 3a, 3b Zone 1: little or no risk Zone 2: low to medium risk Zone 3a: high risk – within areas already built up Zone 3b: high risk – undeveloped and sparsely developed areas including functional flood plains
Wales	Draft TAN15 Development and Flood Risk, July 2003 (National Assembly for Wales, 2003a,b)	Zones A, B, C1, C2 Zone A: little or no risk Zone B: low to medium risk Zone C1: high risk – defended Zone C2: high risk – undefended
Northern Ireland	PPS 15 Planning and Flood Risk (Department of the Environment, in preparation)	Not yet defined

The application of this risk-based approach requires rational assessment of the level of flood risk, in terms both of the development site itself being flooded, and of the development increasing the flood risk to others. As described later in this chapter, developers are responsible for carrying out an appropriate level of flood risk assessment in relation to their proposals. Additionally, higher level national, regional or sub-regional flood studies exist in many areas (Box 4.2). Such studies, where they exist, can be an important part of the FRA process for a given site.

Box 4.2   *Hierarchy of flood risk assessment studies*

Type of study	Scale	Objective of study	Responsible parties
National flood plain mapping programmes	National or regional indicative flood plain mapping	To identify the extent of areas at risk of flooding nationally and regionally	Flood defence agency
Catchment Flood Management Plan (CFMP)	Catchment	To identify flood risk issues and flood alleviation strategies on a catchment scale	Flood defence agency
Strategic flood risk assessment (SFRA)	Catchment or district	To identify flood risk issues on a sub-regional scale for development plans	Local planning authority
Flood risk assessment (FRA)	Individual site or development	To identify and address flood risk issues associated with an individual development	Developer

4.3   PARTIES TO FLOOD RISK AND PLANNING

The effective management of flood risk through the planning process requires contributions from a range of parties, outlined in Table 4.2. In relation to proposals for construction or development, the primary parties typically include:

- developers and others involved in development such as architects, builders etc
- local planning authorities (LPAs)
- flood defence agencies (FDAs)
- sewerage undertakers and canal operators
- other consultees.

The roles and responsibilities of each party are described in the following sections. FDAs vary throughout the United Kingdom, as described in Appendix A1.

Table 4.2 *Key responsibilities relating to flood risk in the planning process*

Organisation	Key responsibilities
Developers and others involved in development	Provision of flood risk assessment and planning application, as required by the LPA
Local planning authorities (LPAs)	Preparing development plans
	Development control
	Administration of Building Regulations
Flood defence agencies (FDAs)	Consultees during the preparation of development plans
	Consultees advising LPAs on flood risk in relation to planning applications
	Note: Some FDAs have their own regulatory powers under the Land Drainage Acts and bye-laws under which consents must be obtained from the FDA. The procedure is quite separate from the planning process
Sewerage undertakers	Public sewerage systems
	Development drainage where this is via adopted sewers
Highways authorities	Highway and road drainage
Canal operators[1]	Canals and some navigable sections of watercourses
Other consultees	Advice on other factors, eg environmental issues
	Note: Riparian landowners can be key consultees for development proposals adjacent to or affecting a watercourse

1 In many cases the canal operator will be British Waterways

4.4 THE ROLE OF THE LOCAL PLANNING AUTHORITY IN MANAGING FLOOD RISK

In England, Wales and Scotland, LPAs have a central role in the operation of the planning system, preparing development plans and determining planning applications. In Northern Ireland, slightly different arrangements apply and planning applications are determined by the Planning Service, which is part of the Department of the Environment. For simplicity in this document the abbreviation LPA is intended to refer to the Planning Service of Northern Ireland as well as LPAs elsewhere.

4.4.1 Development planning

In the context of flood risk management, the primary role of the LPA is to guide, regulate and control development. At the strategic level, county councils and unitary authorities produce Structure Plans and Part 1 Unitary Development Plans (UDPs) respectively. Throughout the United Kingdom, national administrations retain powers to intervene in the development plan preparation process. Under the Planning and Compulsory Purchase Bill, which is currently before Parliament, it is proposed to replace the present system of Structure Plans, Local Plans and Unitary Development Plans with one that comprises regional spatial strategies and local development frameworks, which will include development plan documents, a statement of community involvement and supplementary planning documents.

LPAs produce Local Plans which set out, within the general context of the Structure Plan, detailed policies and specific proposals for the development and use of land (Moore, 2002). In unitary authority areas, Part 2 UDPs are broadly equivalent to the Local Plans.

The selection of areas for development proposed in Local Plans should take account of flood risk using the risk-based method and the relevant national planning policies described in Section 4.2. The assessment of flood risk during the preparation of development plans is usually based on national flood mapping programmes (such as the indicative flood maps produced by the Environment Agency or Scottish Environment Protection Agency) or on strategic flood risk assessments commissioned by the LPA. The scale of these assessments means that the mapping of flood plains may be of limited accuracy and not all relevant flood risk issues may be covered for all sites. **The fact that a development plan identifies an area as suitable for development does not necessarily preclude the requirement that the developer should carry out a site-specific flood risk assessment for that site.**

The role of development plans in contributing to the management of flood risk is described in detail in the relevant national planning policy guidance. In general, while development plans will seek to discourage development in areas assessed to be at risk of flooding, there may be circumstances when new development in these areas may be acceptable to the LPA. This may be because of economic or social benefits associated with such development, particularly where brownfield sites are being redeveloped. However, such circumstances are very much the exception, not the norm.

The importance of development plans in relation to individual planning applications lies in the requirement that, where the plan contains relevant policies, applications shall be determined in accordance with the plan, unless material considerations indicate otherwise.

4.4.2 Development control

When proposals are made for new development, or the redevelopment of an existing site, the LPA will determine the planning application submitted by the developer. The planning process may comprise the following principal stages, which are described in more detail below:

- initial consultation with the LPA – recommended in all cases

- application for outline planning permission – an option which developers may consider in some circumstances

- application for full planning permission

- consultation – the LPA will consult relevant bodies including the FDA(s) where necessary

- determination of the application – unless the application is "called in" for determination at national government level, the LPA will either grant planning permission, possibly with conditions, or will refuse permission.

If an applicant is dissatisfied with the LPA's decision, or the LPA fails to determine the application within the prescribed period, the applicant can appeal to the relevant minister (such as the Secretary of State in England). A local public inquiry, or a less formal hearing, may be held before an appeal is determined.

Initial consultation with the LPA

National planning policy guidance advises LPAs to ensure that, within areas of flood risk identified by the FDA, applicants are informed of this fact when, or preferably before, they submit a planning application. Clearly, this can be done only when the potential applicant first contacts the LPA, and is one reason why **developers should begin pre-application discussions with the LPA as soon as they have identified a site of interest.** LPAs will be able to advise potential applicants how to contact the relevant FDA(s).

LPAs should also be prepared to discuss the requirements that applicants will be expected to meet to satisfy the LPA and FDA on the flood risk and runoff implications of the proposed development. Such discussions should cover the possibility of flood risks to the site, or elsewhere as a result of the development, even if the site is not within the areas of flood risk identified by the FDA. These requirements should be established at the earliest possible stage, so that potential applicants can assess and plan the work required, including the preparation of any necessary flood risk assessment. The LPA will also be able to advise whether an environmental impact assessment will be required.

Application for outline planning permission

Where the permission sought is for the erection of a building, an application may be made for outline planning permission. The granting of outline permission constitutes a commitment by the LPA to the principle of the development, subject to later approval of specified reserved matters. However, such reserved matters are restricted to the siting, design, external appearance, means of access and landscaping of the site. Therefore, any application for outline planning permission, where flood risk is likely to be a material consideration, will need to be supported by a flood risk assessment which provides sufficient information to enable the LPA to determine the application in principle.

Application for full planning permission

It is in the interest of all parties that a developer submitting a planning application submits sufficiently comprehensive information on flood risk, and any proposed mitigation measures, with the planning application. Failure to submit a FRA with the appropriate level of detail is likely to result in refusal of planning permission. This highlights the advantage of early consultation between the developer and the LPA to allow the LPA to guide the developer on the significance of flood risk to development planning on the site, and the need for an appropriate FRA to support any application.

Consultation

Upon receipt of a planning application that may have flood risk implications, the LPA may consult with the FDA and any other relevant bodies. For applications where sufficient information has been provided to indicate that the site is not associated with significant flood risk, the LPA may not need to consult directly with the FDA, but may respond based on standing advice provided by the FDA for such circumstances. If flood risk issues are indicated to be significant (or if there is inadequate information with the application), it is likely that the LPA will directly consult the FDA. The FDAs may comment in terms of both strategic and site-specific issues and, in particular, they are likely to comment on the adequacy of the FRA and the acceptability, from the flood defence point of view, of any proposed mitigation measures.

Determination of the application

The LPA's decision on a planning application will be in accordance with national and local planning policies and will be dependent on a wide range of material considerations, of which flood risk is only one. The statutory requirement is that, where the development plan for the area contains relevant policies, applications will be determined in accordance with the plan, unless material considerations indicate otherwise. Against this background, the LPA will have regard to the information provided with the application (Section 4.5), and the results of the consultations (Section 4.6).

If planning permission is granted it may be subject to conditions. Planning conditions can be used to enhance the quality of a development and enable many development proposals to proceed where it would otherwise have been necessary to refuse planning permission. This will often be the case where such conditions are included in planning approvals in order to manage flood risks. Ideally any such conditions will have been provisionally agreed between the applicant and planning officers before the formal determination of the application, but such officers cannot commit their authority in advance of the elected members' decision.

In relation to the management of flood risk, it should be noted that planning permission is, in many cases, not the only consent required. The FDAs have their own powers to control works that directly affect watercourses; the detailed powers varying with the type of watercourse, its location, and the nature of the work proposed (Appendix A1).

4.5   THE ROLE OF THE DEVELOPER IN MANAGING FLOOD RISK

When developers are planning and designing a development, it is important that flood risk issues be considered, in terms of the risk and consequences of the site itself being flooded and in relation to flood risk elsewhere being affected by the development.

To plan and design developments effectively, developers need to be aware of national planning policy guidance (Appendices A1 to A4), as this sets the context within which any planning application will be considered. Developers also need to have particular regard to the policies set out in the current development plan, in relation to the site in question, and whether that plan has been prepared, or updated, to reflect the current requirements of national and regional planning policy guidance.

Where the development plan has been prepared, or updated, taking account of national and local planning policy guidance on flood risk, the implications for the development proposal should be clear. Nevertheless in relevant cases, the developer will wish to consider the flood risk issues in more detail than these might be dealt with in the plan, in order to prepare detailed proposals which will be acceptable to the LPA and the FDA. Where the development plan has not yet been updated to reflect the current national guidance, the developer will be expected to provide the LPA with sufficient information to allow the application to be determined in accordance with current policies.

Those proposing specific developments are responsible for:

- providing an assessment of whether the proposed development is likely to be affected by flooding and whether it will affect flood risk elsewhere

- satisfying the LPA that any flood risk to the development, or additional flood risk elsewhere arising from the proposal, will be successfully managed with minimum environmental effect, to ensure the site can be developed and used safely.

An understanding of the risk-based approach, inherent in the national planning policy guidance, will aid the developer in meeting these objectives by identifying appropriate and sustainable development options for the site in question. In particular, at the very start of the development design process, the developer should establish:

- the category of flood risk zone (as defined in the appropriate national planning policy guidance) within which the site sits

- whether the LPA or the FDA considers that the site may be subject to any significant flood risk constraints

- the policy of the LPA regarding proposed development in the relevant flood risk category.

The most effective way for developers to identify whether these issues are likely to have a major effect on the type and nature of development that will be permitted, is to engage in pre-application consultation with the LPA and FDA at the earliest possible stage. In these early consultations the developer should discuss with the LPA the requirements they will be expected to satisfy, in terms of information related to the assessment of flood risk that should be included with any planning application.

The developer should also seek to understand any other requirements that the LPA may have with regard to a planning application, for instance whether or not an environmental impact assessment will be required. In consultation with the FDA the developer should seek information about potential risks to their development, about the likely effect on flood risk elsewhere, and on whether mitigation of flood risk is likely to be an acceptable option in principle.

For any site where flood risk is a potential concern, the LPA will expect a flood risk assessment to be submitted with the planning application. The developer is responsible for undertaking or commissioning the FRA. Failure to submit a FRA, or submission of a FRA that does not provide sufficient detail in relation to the relevant issues, is likely to lead to a delay in determining the applications, or may result in refusal of planning permission.

It is in the developer's interest to identify, as soon as possible, whether a FRA will be required, and the appropriate level of detail. Further guidance on the FRA process is given in Chapter 5.

Once a potential flooding issue is identified, it is recommended that the developer undertakes or commissions an initial FRA immediately. This provides an opportunity to minimise abortive expenditure if the site should prove to be unsuitable for the proposed development because of unacceptable flood risks.

Where flood risk is a significant issue, but the developer wishes to pursue some form of development, further consultations with the LPA and FDAs are recommended. It is likely that a more detailed level of FRA, including consideration of the management of runoff from the site, will be required at this stage. It is the responsibility of the developer to undertake or commission such investigations with a view to preparing proposals which will be acceptable to the LPA/FDA. Potential developers need to give early consideration to the likely cost, and time required, to undertake a detailed flood risk assessment. The time could extend to several months in a typical case involving assessment of flood risks, management of runoff from the site, and outline consideration of possible mitigation measures. The results of the FRA, together with details of any proposed mitigation measures, should be submitted in support of any formal planning application.

As noted in Section 4.4.2, applicants who are refused planning permission, or who are granted permission subject to conditions which they find unacceptable, or who do not have their applications determined within the appropriate period, may appeal to the relevant national government department. Time limits for the determination of planning applications, submission of appeals etc, are prescribed by national regulations.

4.6   THE ROLE OF FLOOD DEFENCE AGENCIES AND OTHER BODIES

During determination of a planning application for a site where flood risk is a potential concern, the LPA will usually consult with the FDA, and any other relevant bodies, to assess the appropriateness of the proposed development. If the application contains sufficient information to indicate that flood risk issues are not significant, the LPA may rely on standing advice from the FDA, and may decide that specific consultation is unnecessary.

Early consultation between the developer and the FDA is recommended to establish the extent of information which they may be able to provide in respect of known flooding problems, records of watercourse levels and flows etc. They may, at that stage, be able to comment on the importance of the site for flood management and the scope of any required FRA.

When consulted by an LPA following receipt of a formal application for planning permission, the FDA will normally be able to advise the LPA on the adequacy of any FRA which accompanied the application, and on the acceptability of any proposed mitigation measures from the flood defence point of view. They may also comment on environmental aspects of the proposals.

Other bodies that may be consulted by the LPA, especially in relation to runoff issues include sewerage undertakers, local authorities and British Waterways.

Any unfavourable responses to consultations received by the LPA are likely to result in delay to the determination of a planning application and may ultimately result in refusal of permission. Therefore, there are obvious benefits to developers in discussing their proposals with potential consultees, especially the FDAs, at an early stage in the planning process. Such early discussions provide an opportunity for the consultees to comment on the proposal and, if appropriate, to indicate the requirements that will have to be met to avoid or manage flood risks to their satisfaction. It is the responsibility of the developer to investigate whether, and if so how, the consultees' objectives can be achieved in a way that will be acceptable to the LPA/FDA.

Further details regarding the roles and responsibilities of FDAs throughout the United Kingdom can be found in Appendix A1.

CHAPTER 4

CHAPTER 4

5 Flood risk assessment

5.1 INTRODUCTION

This Chapter describes a recommended methodology for undertaking flood risk assessments to allow consideration of flooding issues relating to development proposals. The chapter is not intended to provide guidance on strategic flood risk assessments (Box 4.2).

The flood risk assessment (FRA) process should not be viewed simply as an administrative hurdle en route to obtaining planning permission. FRA should be an integral part of development design, which should facilitate the promotion of sustainable developments. Flood risk issues may influence the viability of a development, and can have a fundamental influence on the design of a development, including the area of land which may be developed, the type of development allowed, development floor levels and the cost of constructing a proposed development. Flood risk issues may lead to the refusal of planning permission and, as such, **early identification of the constraints and opportunities at a development site due to flood risk issues is crucial if timely and efficient planning and implementation of development proposals is to occur.** For this reason, an initial FRA should be carried out as soon as a site is considered for development.

5.2 FLOOD RISK AND SUSTAINABLE DEVELOPMENT

Some of the key features which influence whether a proposed development will be sustainable in flood risk terms are described in this section. Box 5.1 summarises the range of issues which may affect the sustainability of a development with regard to flood risk, and these issues should be considered within a FRA.

Box 5.1   *Key aims for a development that is sustainable in flood risk terms*

- the development should not be at a significant risk of flooding, and should not be susceptible to damage due to flooding
- the development should not be exposed to flood risk such that the health, safety and welfare of the users of the development, or the population elsewhere, is threatened
- normal operation of the development should not be susceptible to disruption as a result of flooding
- safe access to and from the development should be possible during flood events
- the development should not increase flood risk elsewhere
- the development should not prevent safe maintenance of watercourses or maintenance and operation of flood defences by the FDA
- the development should not be associated with an onerous or difficult operation and maintenance regime to manage flood risk; the responsibility for any operation and maintenance required should be clearly defined.
- future users of the development should be made aware of any flood risk issues relating to the development
- the development design should be such that future users will not have difficulty obtaining insurance or mortgage finance, or in selling all or part of the development, as a result of flood risk issues
- the development should not lead to degradation of the environment.
- the development should meet all of the above criteria for its entire lifetime, including consideration of the potential effects of climate change.

It is essential that proposed developments are sustainable (Box 5.1) and do not compromise the health and safety of the occupants and users of the development. Developments that are frequently visited or occupied by people should be designed so that safe access to and from the development is possible during a flood event. In most cases, safe access can only be provided if there is an access route from the development to an area outside the flood risk zone that is located above flood defence level (see below) and which can be passed along easily by all users. For most developments, especially residential, commercial and industrial developments, it is also important that the emergency services can have safe access to and from the development during the design flood.

The ideal development proposal will be one in which the development is located within an area of little or no risk as defined by national planning policy guidance (Appendix A1). However, if this is not possible and development within a flood risk zone can be justified having regard to other considerations, the feasibility of mitigation measures can be explored. The key objectives of mitigation measures for the principal impacts of flooding are given in Table 5.1 and are described in more detail below.

Table 5.1 *Objectives of flood risk mitigation measures*

Impact	Objective of mitigation measures
Flooding of development	To reduce the risk of the development being flooded and to ensure continued operation and safety during flood events
Change in surface water runoff	To ensure that flood risk downstream of a site is not increased by increased runoff rates and volumes as a result of development
Change in upstream water levels	To ensure that the development does not cause an unacceptable increase in upstream water levels
Change in downstream water levels	To ensure that there is no net loss of flood storage at any flood level up to and including the design flood level

The mitigation measures that may be used to address these issues are outlined in Appendix A3, and a combination of these measures may be required for any site. **In general, developments that rely on mitigation measures to manage flood risk should be avoided.** All mitigation measures have a residual risk of failure, and the requirement for mitigation measures can have major implications on the technical and economic feasibility of developments. These issues must be addressed as part of the FRA process.

Flooding of the development

In most situations, a development which is proposed, despite the fact that it is located in an area that is at risk of flooding, should be designed to prevent flooding of the development during flood events up to and including the design flood event.

When assessing the flood risk to a proposed development it is necessary to appreciate that estimates of flood hazards often are associated with a significant degree of uncertainty. This means that a cautious approach should be taken when interpreting flood hazard information, and allowance should be made for the uncertainty in the flood prediction. For this reason it is common to include an allowance above the design flood level when specifying the level to which the development should be protected from flooding (the flood defence level). This allowance is commonly referred to as freeboard, especially when associated with flood defences (Box 5.2). The allowance to be made at any particular site should be agreed with the FDA.

Box 5.2 *Allowance for uncertainties in the assessment of design flood level*

Flood defences are typically designed to achieve a flood defence level, where:

Flood defence level = design flood level + freeboard allowance.

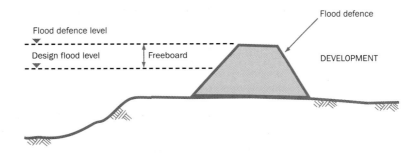

Flood defences typically incorporate a specific freeboard allowance to allow for uncertainty in the design flood level. The amount of freeboard should take account of:

● the level of uncertainty associated with the design flood estimate

● the sensitivity of the flood level to changes in the conditions assumed to prevail during the design flood

● the consequences of overtopping of the defences.

An allowance may also be made for future settlement of the defence structures.

In the past the total freeboard allowance was typically 300 mm for floodwalls and 500 mm for embankments. FDAs typically recommend that the finished floor levels of developments are at least 600 mm above estimated design flood levels.

The Fluvial Freeboard Design Guide (Kirby and Ash, 2000) provides several techniques to allow a suitable freeboard for a particular fluvial flood defence structure to be identified, taking account of local conditions.

While most new developments should be designed so that flooding of the development will not occur during the design flood event, in some cases the potential consequences of flooding may be such that the development, or parts of the development, may be allowed to flood (Appendices A3.3.2 and A3.3.3). In these circumstances suitable mitigation measures (Appendix A3) should be employed to manage the flood risk, to the satisfaction of the FDA.

There is a chance that during the design life of a development, one or more events will occur which are in excess of the design event, or that a flood defence may fail. For this reason, a well-designed development will include measures to minimise the impact that such events could have on the development.

Change in surface-water runoff

All developments, even those that lie outside flood risk zones, may lead to an increase in downstream flood risk due to increased runoff rates and volumes. For this reason, all new developments should be designed so that runoff from the development is considered and, if appropriate, controlled.

Change in upstream water levels

A development that obstructs flood flows will cause an increase in flood levels upstream of the site, which may increase flood risk to existing or future developments. If the development is proposed within an area that conveys flood flows, careful design will be required to ensure that an unacceptable increase in upstream water levels does not occur (Section 3.3.3). In general, the presumption is that a proposed development should not cause any increase in upstream water levels. However, in certain circumstances the FDA may allow some small increase in upstream water levels if the area upstream of the proposed development is not sensitive to such changes. The FDA should be consulted to confirm whether any small increase in upstream water levels would be permitted for any particular development site.

Change in downstream water levels

A development which results in any reduction in the volume of flood water that can be temporarily stored on the site during a flood event will cause an increase in the peak flood flow downstream. This will result in an increase in flood levels downstream of the site (Section 3.3.4). It can often be shown that the downstream effect of loss of flood plain storage due to an individual development would be very small. However, the potential cumulative effect of a series of developments is such that it is important to ensure that each individual development does not lead to a net loss of flood storage. It is therefore usually necessary to provide equivalent new flood storage to replace the volume that would otherwise be lost due to any development (Appendix A3.3.10).

5.3   FLOOD RISK ASSESSMENT METHODOLOGY

5.3.1   Introduction

This section describes the general methodology to be followed in the FRA process. Detailed advice on how to undertake each step of the FRA process for the range of flooding issues that may occur at development sites is given in Appendix A2. Appendix A3 provides information on the types of mitigation measures which may be applied at sites where flood risk is an issue.

A FRA toolkit which provides guidance on the steps to be taken in a FRA, and on how to interpret the results of FRAs when considering the appropriateness of a proposed development, is provided in Chapter 6 of this guide. It is recommended that Chapter 6 is used when undertaking a FRA. The following sections describe the rationale underpinning the tiered approach to FRA.

5.3.2   Overview

Where a FRA is required as part of the development control process, it is vital that an appropriate FRA is submitted with the planning application so that the local planning authority (LPA) can make an informed decision on whether to grant planning permission (Section 4.4.2).

There are three key objectives of a FRA:

- to assess the flood risk to the proposed development, and to demonstrate the feasibility of appropriately designing the development such that any residual flood risk to the development, and its users, would be acceptable

- to assess the potential impact of the proposed development on flood risk elsewhere, and to demonstrate the feasibility of appropriately designing the development such that the development would not increase flood risk elsewhere

- to satisfy the requirements of national planning policy guidance, which require FRAs to be submitted in support of planning applications (Appendix A1).

The aim of a FRA is to ensure that if a proposed development is implemented, flood risk will not be increased, either to the new development or elsewhere, and that the proposed development is consistent with national planning policy guidance (Appendix A1). An FRA should consider the issues that influence the acceptability of a development in terms of flood risk, and should either produce an acceptable development proposal or a conclusion that a proposed development is unacceptable due to flood risk issues. Acceptable development proposals will meet a number of key criteria (Box 5.1) and will have an FRA report that demonstrates that these criteria have been met. When assessing the adequacy of a proposed development it is recommended that the flowcharts in Chapter 6, in conjunction with the relevant national planning policy guidance and any relevant supplementary guidance, are reviewed.

A FRA should be carried out under the direction of a qualified and competent professional. Appendix A4 provides contact details of professional institutions which may be able to recommend organisations who can provide specialist advice.

It is recommended that an appropriate level of FRA is carried out as soon as a site is considered for development. An initial FRA can be extremely useful in identifying the viability of a potential development site and guiding development proposals at an early stage, and it is strongly recommended that this is undertaken before purchasing any site. As development proposals progress, additional FRAs can be undertaken to inform the master planning and outline design process. These will be at increasing levels of detail, as appropriate. This guide defines three levels of FRA which can be undertaken. The three levels of FRA are summarised in Table 5.2 and discussed in more detail in Sections 5.3.3 to 5.3.5.

Table 5.2   *Levels of flood risk assessment*

FRA Level	Description
1	**Screening study** to identify whether there are any flooding issues related to a development site which may warrant further consideration.
2	**Scoping study** to be undertaken if the Level 1 study indicates that the site may lie within an area which is at risk of flooding or that the site may increase flood risk due to increased runoff, to confirm the possible sources of flooding which may affect the site. The study should include the following objectives: • assessment of the availability and adequacy of existing information • qualitative assessment of the flood risk to the site, and the impact of the site on flood risk elsewhere • assessment of the possible scope for appropriate development design and to scope additional work required.
3	**Detailed study** to be undertaken if the Level 2 study concludes that quantitative analysis is required to assess flood risk issues related to the development site. The study should include: • quantitative assessment of the potential flood risk to the development • quantitative assessment of the potential impact of development site on flood risk elsewhere • quantitative demonstration of the effectiveness of any proposed mitigation measures.

A Level 1 FRA should be undertaken for all potential sources of flood risk for a development site (Section 2.2). The potential impact of the proposed development on existing flood defences, and the potential impact of increased runoff due to the development, should also be considered. The scope of work for a Level 2 FRA will depend on the findings of the Level 1 FRA. This in turn will allow the scope of work required for a Level 3 FRA to be assessed. The nature of the flood hazard, the sensitivity of the proposed development, the potential impact it may have on flood risk elsewhere, and the amount of existing information will influence how many levels of the FRA process will have to be undertaken for a development.

Figure 5.1 shows a flowchart summarising the key levels in the FRA process. **Chapter 6 provides further guidance on the tiered FRA process.**

The FRA process should take into account any likely future expansion of the development, operation and maintenance issues and the possible impact of climate change (Box 5.3) which may occur during the lifetime of the development.

Box 5.3   *Consideration of climate change in the FRA process*

The potential effects of climate change (Section 2.3) should be allowed for in an FRA, as recommended by current national planning policy guidance (Appendix A1).

Estimation of potential climate change impacts is an area of current and ongoing research, and climate change allowances may alter depending on the situation. It is recommended that the allowances which are to be made for climate change within an FRA should be agreed with the LPA/FDA as part of the FRA process.

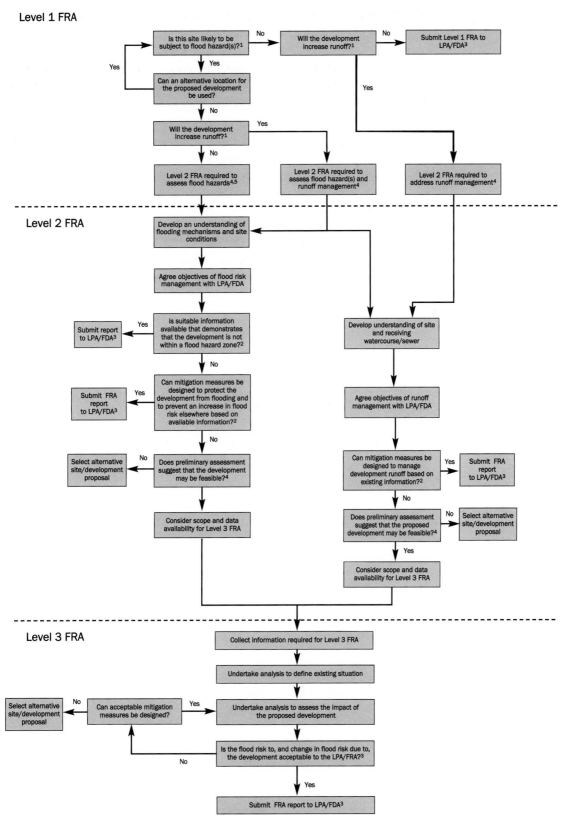

Figure 5.1 *FRA process for development proposals*

Notes

1. If existing information is inadequate the precautionary approach should be adopted and a "Yes" answer should be assumed.
2. If existing information is inadequate the precautionary approach should be adopted and a "No" answer should be assumed.
3. It is recommended that the findings of the FRA are discussed with the LPA/FDA prior to formal submission of the report.
4. Development proposals should be progressed only if the proposals are likely to be consistent with those of sustainable development, as defined in relevant planning policies.
5. If the site is a brownfield site, it is likely to be beneficial to demonstrate that the proposed development will reduce runoff rates and volumes compared to the existing situation and a Level 2 FRA of surface water management is therefore recommended.

It is important that the LPA and FDA are consulted at all levels of the FRA process (Box 5.4).

Box 5.4   *Consultation in the FRA process*

Consultation is an essential part of the FRA Process. Consultation can:

- help define the requirements related to any individual development
- allow early identification of the likely acceptability of any proposals
- assist in the identification of useful information
- allow local knowledge and experience to be utilised in the FRA process.

Consultation with the LPA/FDA

It is recommended that consultation is undertaken as soon as a site is considered for development, and that consultation should be ongoing throughout the FRA process.

Initially, consultation should be undertaken with the (LPA). The LPA should be able to provide guidance on current national planning policy guidance and also on any local supplementary advice and information that may be available (including strategic flood risk assessments). The LPA should also be able to provide contacts in the relevant (FDA).

Consultation with the FDA is usually very valuable, as the FDA can often provide information of any existing relevant national or local technical guidance, existing information on flood risk at the site, known or potential flooding problems and issues in an area, any proposed strategic flood risk management plans for the area, and advice on methods which may be acceptable for mitigation of flood risk issues.

In cases where the sensitivity of the proposed development is low, and where the development may have a small impact on flood risk elsewhere, the LPA may wish to provide advice and review proposals without a site-specific referral to the FDA. As the degree of involvement of the LPA and FDA will vary between development proposals, the term LPA/FDA is used in this document. Appendix A1 identifies the FDAs within each part of the United Kingdom.

Consultation with other responsible bodies

In some circumstances consultation with other responsible bodies, such as sewerage undertakers and canal operators, may provide similar benefits to those discussed above for the LPA/FDA (Table 4.2).

Consultation with the insurance and mortgage industry

It is recommended that consultation is undertaken as soon as a site is considered for development, and that consultation should be ongoing throughout the FRA process. Insurers may require a higher standard of protection than the FDA if normal insurance cover is to be provided (Section 3.2.3).

Consultation with the local community

The local community can be a very useful source of information for FRAs. Local residents and community groups may hold information on past events and may be able to provide eye witness accounts of previous flood events. Some communities may have a designated flood warden, who may be able to provide useful local knowledge.

5.3.3   Level 1 flood risk assessment

A Level 1 FRA should be carried out for all development sites, unless the LPA advise that a FRA is not required. The discussion below provides generic guidance on undertaking a Level 1 FRA. Additional details on the work required and information sources available for specific types of flood risk can be found in Appendix A2.

Objectives

The objective of the Level 1 FRA process is to:

- develop an understanding of the potential flood risk to a development site

- agree with the LPA what aspects of flood risk would need to be addressed in a more detailed flood risk assessment.

Information Sources

A Level 1 FRA involves a review of publicly available information and consultation with the LPA/FDA to identify in broad terms what issues related to flood risk need to be considered (eg fluvial, tidal, groundwater, increase in runoff etc).

The first stage of a Level 1 FRA should be to review the national planning policy guidance relevant to development and flood risk and to ascertain whether the LPA/FDA have any supplementary planning guidance or information which is relevant to flood risk at the site (Box 5.4).

Output

The key questions to be addressed in this level are summarised in Table 5.3. Adoption of the precautionary principle (Box 4.1) means that where there is any uncertainty regarding the likely presence of any of these potential sources of flooding, a more detailed assessment should be undertaken. This might perhaps initially involve a walkover survey by an experienced professional. If an element of doubt still remains, the FRA should proceed to Level 2.

Table 5.3 *Level 1 flood risk assessment: key questions*

Is the site likely to be at risk of flooding from (Appendix A2.1): a watercourse, the sea, an estuary, groundwater, overland flow, an artificial drainage system, infrastructure failure?

Is the proposed development likely to obstruct the maintenance access requirements of the FDA or affect the integrity of an existing flood defence? (Appendix A2.1.2)

Is the proposed development likely to increase flood risk elsewhere due to increased runoff rates and volumes from the site? (Appendix A2.1.3)

Given the above, the nature of the development, and the initial advice of the FDA and LPA and taking other factors into consideration, is continued promotion of a possible development at the site appropriate?

The key output of a Level 1 FRA is the identification of the flood risk issues which require more consideration for a site.

A flowchart summarising the work to be undertaken during a Level 1 FRA is provided in Section 6.1.

5.3.4

Level 2 flood risk assessment

A Level 2 FRA should be undertaken for each potential flood risk issue that is identified as being associated with a site during a Level 1 FRA (Box 5.5). The discussion below provides generic guidance on undertaking a Level 2 FRA. Additional details on the work required and information sources available for specific types of flood risk can be found in Appendix A2.

Objectives

The objectives of the Level 2 FRA process are to:

- develop an understanding of the mechanisms of flooding at the site

- develop an understanding of the proposed development site within the context of the catchment or coastal cell

- identify available data

- confirm whether the site is likely to be in a "little or no risk", "low to medium" or "high" flood risk zone (Appendix A1)

- produce a preliminary qualitative assessment of the potential impact of, and constraints to, the proposed development

- develop an understanding of the potential development design that may be employed at the site

- define the additional work required to produce a Level 3 FRA (if necessary).

When undertaking a Level 2 FRA it is vital that the potential interaction of different flooding hazards is considered so that the potential for cumulative effects and effects in combination are assessed.

At this level decisions can be made about the likely feasibility of the proposed development, and in some situations, if sufficient data is available, it may be possible to produce a sufficiently detailed flood risk assessment to submit with a planning application.

Information sources

In order for a Level 2 FRA to be undertaken, some site survey information will be required. The survey should be sufficient to provide information on the general ground levels across the site, and should include surveys of the levels of any formal or informal flood defences relevant to the site.

As part of a Level 2 FRA, Ordnance Survey maps and any available site survey should be reviewed and a walkover survey undertaken to assess the mechanisms by which flooding of the site could occur. If possible, the site should be visited during or immediately after a flood event. During the site walkover it may be possible to identify the sources of flooding, the likely routes that would be followed by flood waters, as well as to develop an understanding of the site's key features and its likely condition during a flood event. Flood defences should be identified. A plan should be produced showing the findings of the walkover survey.

It is important that the LPA/FDA and any other body which may have information on flood risk are consulted during this level of the FRA process. It is recommended that the standard of protection required for the proposed development is confirmed at the start of this level of the FRA process, and that all available flood risk information is obtained. Other data sources may also assist in determining likely flood conditions at the site (Appendix A2). If appropriate data are found it may be possible to use this to define design conditions without the need for extensive modelling studies.

Box 5.5 *Case history – Level 2 fluvial flood risk assessment*

A town centre site was to be redeveloped to include new office buildings and a basement car park. The site was located near to several watercourses and a flood risk assessment was required to identify whether the risk of fluvial flooding at the site was sufficient to warrant a more detailed hydrological and hydraulic study.

A walkover survey was undertaken to assess potential flood hazards and mechanisms at the site. Historic information was collected from various sources including the local water company, the local authority and the Environment Agency and a library search was undertaken. The library search identified a very useful local history book which contained a lot of historical information about past flood events in the town. The historic information was used to reinforce the information provided by the Environment Agency.

Based on the available information, it was concluded that the site was at an acceptable risk of flooding from the watercourses in the vicinity of the site. However, the proposed basement car parks were identified as being at risk of flooding from a variety of other hazards. These areas would potentially be vulnerable to the ingress of groundwater, overland flow flooding from low lying paved areas around the site and localised flooding due to sewer surcharge. Mitigation measures were proposed to protect the basement areas from these flooding hazards.

Output

If the work described above suggests that the proposed development may be within a flood risk area then consideration should be given to identifying an alternative development site. If this is not practicable, and the proposed development of the site is to be pursued, a preliminary qualitative assessment of the feasibility of the development design should be undertaken (Appendix A3). If the preliminary consideration of mitigation measures suggests that development may be feasible, the work required to undertake a full detailed (Level 3) FRA can be assessed.

If a site is subject to flood hazard from more than one type of flooding, it may be that a Level 2 FRA will be adequate to address flood risk issues associated with one or more of the flood hazards, but a Level 3 FRA may be required to address flood risk issues associated with other types. The work required to undertake a Level 3 FRA will depend upon the nature of the proposed development, the issues which need to be addressed and the nature of existing information on flood risk at the site. If further work is required then it may be advantageous to submit a Level 2 FRA report to the LPA/FDA to obtain agreement as to the potential viability both of the proposed development and the proposed methodology for the Level 3 FRA.

If sufficient information has been obtained and reviewed during the Level 2 FRA to allow the outline design of the development to be progressed to an adequate level of detail, it may be possible to submit a Level 2 FRA report in support of a planning application. A Level 2 FRA report will often provide an adequate level of detail for a development in a low to medium flood risk zone, unless the development is of such a type that national planning policy guidance recommends that such development should be avoided in low to medium risk zones (Appendix A1). Level 2 FRAs may provide sufficient information for the support of an outline planning application subject to the LPA confirming that the information provided will be adequate to allow it to determine the application in principle (Section 4.4.2).

If it is considered that sufficient information exists to fully assess flood risk issues relating to a proposed development, the Level 2 FRA report should contain the same information as a Level 3 FRA (Box 5.6). It is recommended that the findings of the Level 2 FRA be discussed with the LPA/FDA before submitting a planning application.

A flowchart summarising the work to be undertaken during a Level 2 FRA is provided in Section 6.2.

5.3.5   Level 3 flood risk assessment

A Level 3 FRA report should provide a quantitative assessment of the flood risk issues identified and scoped in FRA Level 2. The scope and methodology required in a Level 3 report will depend on the findings of a Level 2 FRA. The discussion below provides generic guidance on undertaking a Level 3 FRA. Additional details on the work required and information sources available for specific types of flood risk can be found in Appendix A2.

Objectives

A Level 3 assessment should be undertaken to such a level of detail that an outline design/masterplan of the development can be presented to the LPA/FDA. Typically, the work required in a Level 3 FRA will involve:

- review of Level 1 and 2 FRAs

- modelling to define the existing flood hazard, including assessment of conditions following expected climate change over the lifetime of the development

- modelling to assess the potential impact of the proposed development

- outline design of mitigation measures (Appendix A3), and associated modelling to demonstrate that the development will not lead to an increase in flood risk elsewhere

- sensitivity testing to demonstrate that the estimates of flood risk to, and arising from, the site are not overly dependent on the assumed model parameters

- preparation of a FRA report.

Information sources

Much of the information required for a Level 3 FRA should have been collected during the Level 1 and Level 2 FRA process. However, it is common for significant topographical and hydrographic survey data to be required during a Level 3 FRA to enable modelling of the situation. In some cases, it may also be desirable to undertake a period of monitoring to improve an understanding of the situation and to obtain data to assist model calibration/verification. Consultation with the LPA/FDA should be undertaken during this stage of the FRA process.

Output

The Level 3 report should be submitted as part of the planning application, although it is recommended that the findings of the report be discussed with the LPA/FDA before submission of a planning application. The recommended contents of a Level 3 FRA are included in Box 5.6. The contents of a Level 3 FRA report should be cross-referenced with the requirements of the relevant planning policy guidance, and any supplementary guidance produced by the LPA and FDA.

Box 5.6 *Recommended contents of a FRA report*

- a description of the existing site, including: topography, levels, land use, location, type and condition of existing flood defences, hydraulic structures

- a description of existing flood risks, including: flood hazards, flood sources, flooding mechanisms, flood routes and historical flood events; expected flood levels, depths, velocities and extents across the site, including an explanation of how they have been derived, for a range of flood probabilities; flood duration and rate of onset of flooding

- a description of the proposed development, including: type of development, proposed floor levels, potential impact of flood risk to, and resulting from, the development in the absence of mitigation measures, including the potential impact of climate change

- a description of proposed mitigation measures: including type of mitigation measures, flood defence levels, description of supporting calculations (if undertaken). Statement on operation and maintenance arrangements for the lifetime of the development

- a summary of: the residual flood risk to the development, the residual impact of the development on flood risk elsewhere, the residual impact of the proposed development on the environment

- an explanation of the purpose of the modelling, where modelling has been carried out, a technical description of the model(s) used, a description of the data sources (including survey) used, details of any calibration/validation undertaken, the key results of the modelling, and the results of sensitivity analyses

Appropriate plans should be included showing existing site conditions, site levels, the areas subject to flood risk, the proposed development, access/evacuation routes and anticipated mitigation measures. An indicative cross-section of the site showing proposed levels of key features and flood levels is also useful.

Any checklists, flowcharts etc (such as the flood risk assessment toolkit given in Section 6) used in the FRA. If appropriate, a summary risk register (Appendix A5).

A flowchart summarising the work to be undertaken during a Level 3 FRA is provided in Section 6.3.

CHAPTER 5

Part C

FLOOD RISK ASSESSMENT TOOLKIT

Part

C

6   Flood risk assessment toolkit

This Chapter contains a number of flowcharts that form a toolkit to provide guidance on the flood risk assessment process. This should assist with the planning of developments, taking into account flood risk issues in an appropriate manner. **The toolkit has been developed to guide the user through the flood risk assessment process.** This toolkit is designed for use by those commissioning, undertaking and assessing flood risk assessments (FRAs) and can be used to determine whether a FRA addresses the range of issues related to flood risk in an appropriate manner. It should also assist in determining whether a proposed development has been designed in a reasonable manner in relation to flood risk issues. This toolkit provides only generic advice on the assessment of flood risk and the advice given should be interpreted in the context of local conditions and planning policy guidance.

The toolkit refers to relevant sections of this guide that provide details on how flood risk assessment and appropriate development design can be progressed.

The flowchart structure is based on the tiered three-level approach to flood risk assessment (Section 5.3). The toolkit is structured in the following manner:

- Checklist A summarises the key issues to be considered when considering the acceptability of a proposed development.

- Section 6.1 summarises the process to be followed for a Level 1 FRA.

- Section 6.2 summarises the process to be followed for a Level 2 FRA.

- Section 6.3 summarises the process to be followed for a Level 3 FRA.

For the sake of clarity the toolkit provides a structure to the flood risk assessment process whereby each potential flooding hazard which may affect a proposed development is assessed in turn. However, it should be appreciated that measures proposed to address the flood risk associated with one hazard may cause impacts on another flood risk issue (Appendix A3.1). For this reason, **it is essential that during any FRA the potential impact of cumulative effects or the impact of effects in combination be considered.**

It is recommended that the user reviews the key issues provided in Checklist A before undertaking a flood risk assessment. Flowchart 1 can then be used to begin the flood risk assessment process.

National planning policy guidance (Appendix A1) makes it clear that the developer is responsible for ensuring the safe development and future occupancy of a proposed development site. While LPAs are required to consider flood risk issues in the public interest, national planning policy guidance (Appendix A1) is clear that the LPA need not undertake their own FRA for a proposed development, but can rely on a FRA submitted by the developer. **It is the developer's responsibility to ensure that an adequate FRA is carried out and submitted with a planning application for review by the LPA/FDA, and to implement any approved flood risk mitigation works recommended within the FRA.** The need for mitigation works should be avoided wherever possible through appropriate planning of development locations.

Estimates of flood risk are usually associated with a considerable degree of uncertainty and should not be regarded as precise predictions. **A suitably cautious approach to decision-making should be followed where flood risk is an issue.**

Notes to accompany flood risk assessment checklist and flowcharts

1 In line with the precautionary principle, if sufficient information is not available a "NO" answer should be assumed.

2 In line with the precautionary principle, if sufficient information is not available then a Level 2 FRA should be undertaken.

3 While the potential impact of an individual development may in some cases be minimal, in order to reduce the potential impact of cumulative effects a "YES" response should be given only with LPA/FDA approval.

4 This should include agreement of the required standard of protection for the proposed development, freeboard requirements, maintenance access requirements, detailed requirements for runoff attenuation, maximum permitted increase in upstream water level (if applicable) etc.

5 Definitions of areas of "little or no risk", "low to medium risk" and "high risk" are given in the relevant planning policy guidance (see Appendix A1).

6 It is recommended that the proposals are discussed with the LPA/FDA before submission of a FRA.

CHECKLIST A: REQUIREMENTS FOR SUSTAINABLE DEVELOPMENT IN RELATION TO FLOOD RISK

The questions below relate to issues that should be considered when determining whether or not a proposed development is likely to be sustainable in flood risk terms. In most cases, a proposed development is unlikely to be considered acceptable unless the answer to all of the questions is "YES".

Criterion	YES[1]	NO
If the proposed development lies within an area that is at risk of flooding under existing conditions, is there good justification for the location of the proposed development?		
Is the standard of protection of the proposed development in agreement with national planning policy guidance and/or the requirements of the LPA/FDA?		
Does the design of the proposed development take into account the potential impact of future climate change over its lifetime?		
Does the design of the proposed development take into account any likely future changes to the nature of the site that may occur over its lifetime?		
Is the residual flood risk to the proposed development from events that are more extreme than the design flood event acceptable?		
Will any anticipated disruption to the normal operation of the proposed development due to flooding be acceptable?		
Has the proposed development been designed so that any risks to health, safety and welfare are appropriately managed?		
Will adequate, safe, access to and from the proposed development be available during floods?		
Are the predicted impacts of the proposed development on upstream flood risk acceptable?		
Are the predicted impacts of the proposed development on downstream flood risk acceptable?		
Will runoff from the proposed development be managed in an appropriate manner?		
Are the potential environmental impacts of the proposed development acceptable?		
Are the operation and maintenance requirements associated with the proposed development acceptable, and is it clear who will be responsible for any required operation and maintenance over the lifetime of the proposed development?		
Has it been ensured that the proposed development will not obstruct any FDA maintenance access?		
Is the design of the proposed development such that it will not compromise any strategic flood risk management plans that the FDA may have for an area?		
Will arrangements be made to ensure that future owners/operators/occupiers of the site will be aware of any residual flood risks, mitigation measures, and operation and maintenance requirements?		
Is the design of the development such that future users will not have difficulty in obtaining insurance or mortgages, or in selling all or part of the development in the future, due to flood risk issues?		
Are any relevant consents or licences required from the FDA likely to be given?		

6.1 LEVEL 1 FLOOD RISK ASSESSMENT

Flowchart 1 provides guidance on the procedures to be followed when undertaking a Level 1 FRA, as part of a tiered three-level approach to flood risk assessment (Section 5.3.2). It is recommended that the reader refers to Checklist A to review the key factors affecting sustainable development and flood risk before undertaking a Level 1 FRA.

Further details on undertaking a Level 1 FRA can be found in Section 5.3.3 and Appendix A2.1.

FLOWCHART 1 　　　　Level 1 flood risk assessment　　　　Sheet 1 of 4

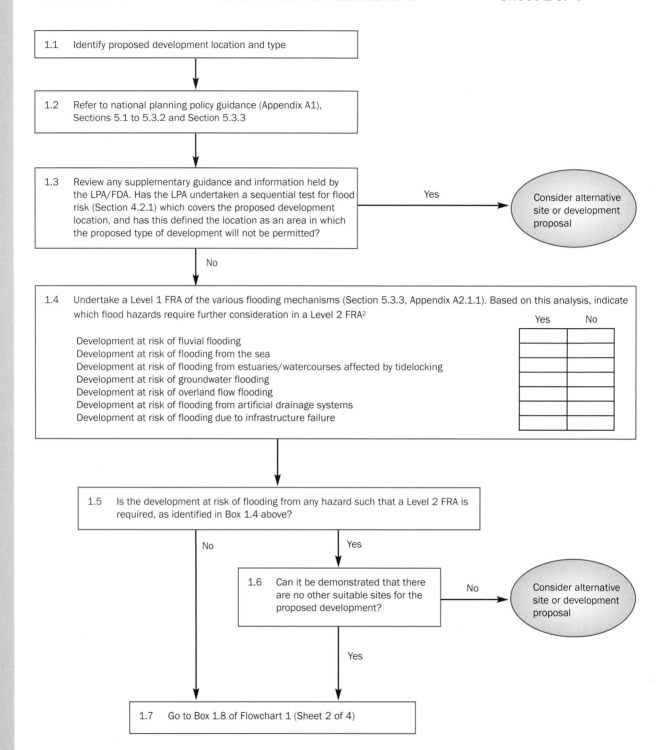

1.1　Identify proposed development location and type

1.2　Refer to national planning policy guidance (Appendix A1), Sections 5.1 to 5.3.2 and Section 5.3.3

1.3　Review any supplementary guidance and information held by the LPA/FDA. Has the LPA undertaken a sequential test for flood risk (Section 4.2.1) which covers the proposed development location, and has this defined the location as an area in which the proposed type of development will not be permitted?

Yes → Consider alternative site or development proposal

No

1.4　Undertake a Level 1 FRA of the various flooding mechanisms (Section 5.3.3, Appendix A2.1.1). Based on this analysis, indicate which flood hazards require further consideration in a Level 2 FRA[2]

Development at risk of fluvial flooding
Development at risk of flooding from the sea
Development at risk of flooding from estuaries/watercourses affected by tidelocking
Development at risk of groundwater flooding
Development at risk of overland flow flooding
Development at risk of flooding from artificial drainage systems
Development at risk of flooding due to infrastructure failure

Yes　No

1.5　Is the development at risk of flooding from any hazard such that a Level 2 FRA is required, as identified in Box 1.4 above?

No

Yes

1.6　Can it be demonstrated that there are no other suitable sites for the proposed development?

No → Consider alternative site or development proposal

Yes

1.7　Go to Box 1.8 of Flowchart 1 (Sheet 2 of 4)

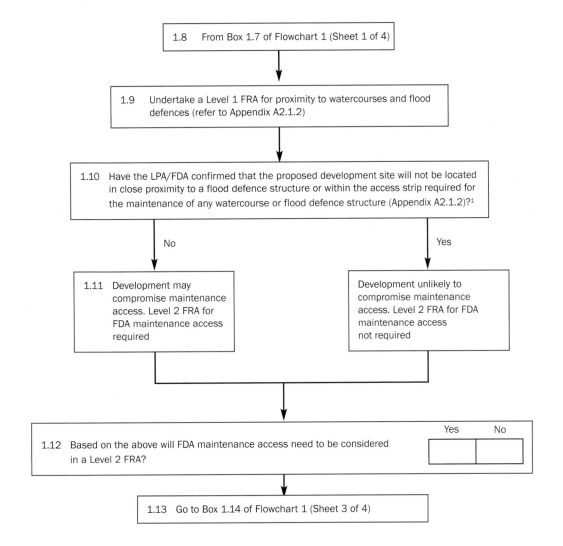

1.8   From Box 1.7 of Flowchart 1 (Sheet 1 of 4)

1.9   Undertake a Level 1 FRA for proximity to watercourses and flood defences (refer to Appendix A2.1.2)

1.10   Have the LPA/FDA confirmed that the proposed development site will not be located in close proximity to a flood defence structure or within the access strip required for the maintenance of any watercourse or flood defence structure (Appendix A2.1.2)?[1]

No

Yes

1.11   Development may compromise maintenance access. Level 2 FRA for FDA maintenance access required

Development unlikely to compromise maintenance access. Level 2 FRA for FDA maintenance access not required

1.12   Based on the above will FDA maintenance access need to be considered in a Level 2 FRA?

Yes	No

1.13   Go to Box 1.14 of Flowchart 1 (Sheet 3 of 4)

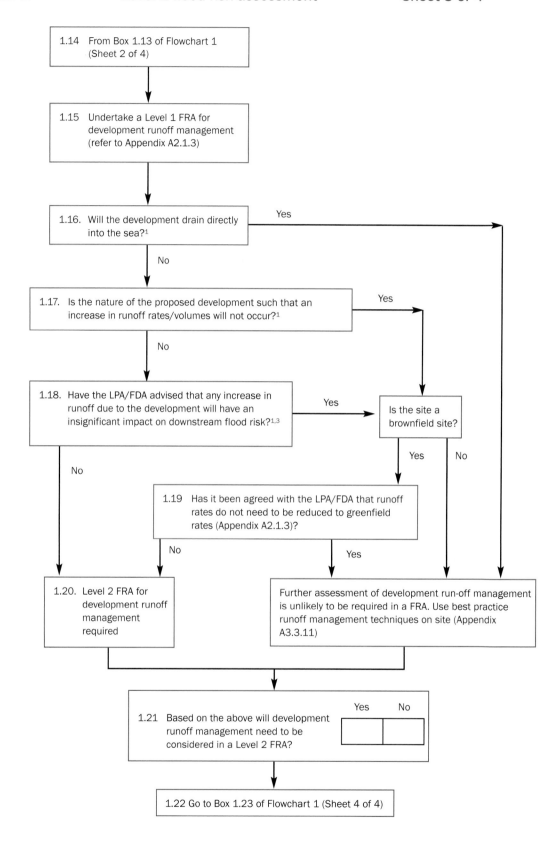

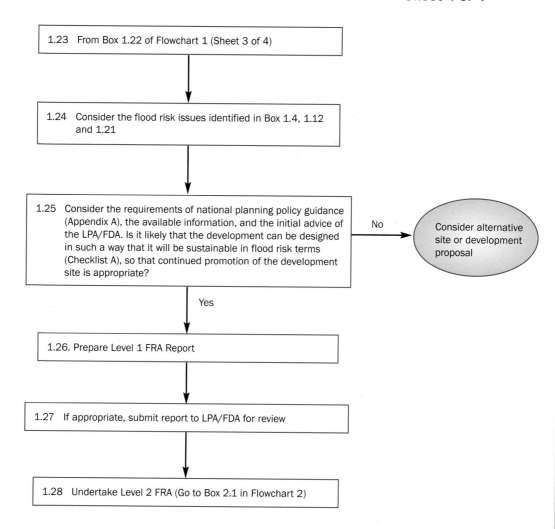

1.23   From Box 1.22 of Flowchart 1 (Sheet 3 of 4)

1.24   Consider the flood risk issues identified in Box 1.4, 1.12 and 1.21

1.25   Consider the requirements of national planning policy guidance (Appendix A), the available information, and the initial advice of the LPA/FDA. Is it likely that the development can be designed in such a way that it will be sustainable in flood risk terms (Checklist A), so that continued promotion of the development site is appropriate?

No → Consider alternative site or development proposal

Yes

1.26. Prepare Level 1 FRA Report

1.27   If appropriate, submit report to LPA/FDA for review

1.28   Undertake Level 2 FRA (Go to Box 2.1 in Flowchart 2)

Part C

CHAPTER 6

6.2 LEVEL 2 FLOOD RISK ASSESSMENT

Flowchart 2 provides guidance on the procedures to follow when undertaking a Level 2 FRA, as part of a tiered three-level approach to flood risk assessment (Section 5.3.2). It is recommended that the reader refers to Section 6.1 before undertaking a Level 2 FRA.

Further details on undertaking a Level 2 FRA can be found in Section 5.3.4 and Appendix A2.2.

2.1 From Box 1.28 of Flowchart 1 (Sheet 4 of 4)

2.2 Review findings of Level 1 FRA (refer to Section 5.3.4 and Appendix A2.1)

2.3 Obtain topographical survey of development site and other useful information (Section 5.3.4, Appendix A2.2)

2.4 Confirm LPA/FDA requirements in relation to the development proposal (Section 5.3.4)[4]

2.5 For each of the flooding hazards identified in Box 1.4, undertake a Level 2 FRA to assess the level of flood risk posed by each hazard (Section 5.3.4, Appendix A2.2)

2.6 Develop an understanding of the potential flooding mechanism(s) at the site

2.7 Identify availability and adequacy of any information that may be of use (Appendix A2.2)

2.8 Based on the available information, is it possible to confirm the design flood level at the proposed development site?[1]

Yes

No

2.9 Need to assess the flood risk associated with the flood hazard in a Level 3 FRA

2.10. Based on the above analysis, indicate the flood risk associated with each of the flooding hazards where known. If sufficient information is not available to confirm the level of flood risk, identify those flood hazards that require further consideration in a Level 3 FRA to define flood levels and risks

Flooding hazard	High Risk[5]	Low to Medium Risk[5]	Little or No Risk[5]	Level 3 FRA required
Fluvial flooding				
Flooding from the sea				
Flooding from estuaries/watercourses affected by tidelocking				
Groundwater flooding				
Overland flow flooding				
Flooding from artificial drainage systems				
Flooding due to infrastructure failure				

2.11 Has a Level 2 FRA been undertaken for each hazard identified in Box 1.4?

No

Yes

2.12 Go to Box 2.13 of Flowchart 2 (Sheet 2 of 3)

Part C

CHAPTER 6

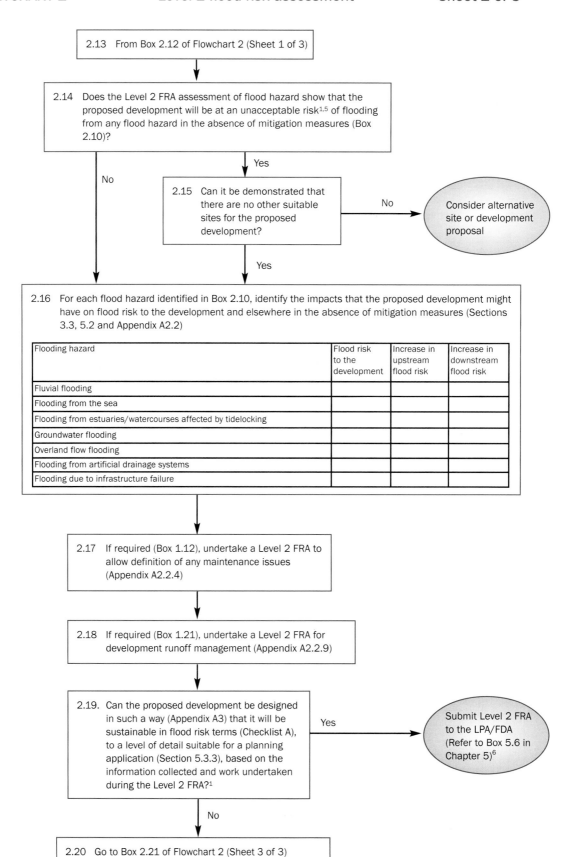

2.13 From Box 2.12 of Flowchart 2 (Sheet 1 of 3)

2.14 Does the Level 2 FRA assessment of flood hazard show that the proposed development will be at an unacceptable risk[1,5] of flooding from any flood hazard in the absence of mitigation measures (Box 2.10)?

Yes

No

2.15 Can it be demonstrated that there are no other suitable sites for the proposed development?

No → Consider alternative site or development proposal

Yes

2.16 For each flood hazard identified in Box 2.10, identify the impacts that the proposed development might have on flood risk to the development and elsewhere in the absence of mitigation measures (Sections 3.3, 5.2 and Appendix A2.2)

Flooding hazard	Flood risk to the development	Increase in upstream flood risk	Increase in downstream flood risk
Fluvial flooding			
Flooding from the sea			
Flooding from estuaries/watercourses affected by tidelocking			
Groundwater flooding			
Overland flow flooding			
Flooding from artificial drainage systems			
Flooding due to infrastructure failure			

2.17 If required (Box 1.12), undertake a Level 2 FRA to allow definition of any maintenance issues (Appendix A2.2.4)

2.18 If required (Box 1.21), undertake a Level 2 FRA for development runoff management (Appendix A2.2.9)

2.19. Can the proposed development be designed in such a way (Appendix A3) that it will be sustainable in flood risk terms (Checklist A), to a level of detail suitable for a planning application (Section 5.3.3), based on the information collected and work undertaken during the Level 2 FRA?[1]

Yes → Submit Level 2 FRA to the LPA/FDA (Refer to Box 5.6 in Chapter 5)[6]

No

2.20 Go to Box 2.21 of Flowchart 2 (Sheet 3 of 3)

Part **C**

CHAPTER 6

2.21   From Box 2.20 of Flowchart 2 (Sheet 2 of 3)

2.22   Consider the requirements of national planning policy guidance (Appendix A1), the available information, and the requirements and advice of the LPA/FDA. Is it likely that the proposed development can be designed in such a way (Appendix A3) that it will be sustainable in flood risk terms (Checklist A) if further detailed assessment is undertaken in a Level 3 FRA?

No → Consider alternative site or development proposal

Yes

2.23   Identify the issues relating to flood hazards that will need to be considered during a Level 3 FRA

Flooding hazard	Flood risk to the development	Increase in upstream flood risk	Increase in downstream flood risk
Fluvial flooding			
Flooding from the sea			
Flooding from estuaries/watercourses affected by tidelocking			
Groundwater flooding			
Overland flow flooding			
Flooding from artificial drainage systems			
Flooding due to infrastructure failure			

Development runoff management
Maintenance access

2.24   Scope further work and survey required in Level 3 FRA (Section 5.3.4, Appendix A2.2, Appendix A2.3)

2.25   Does the developer consider that a Level 3 FRA would be worthwhile, having regard to:
- the potential benefit of the proposed development
- the estimated costs and timescales of such a study
- the risk that a Level 3 FRA will find that the proposed development will not be acceptable in flood risk terms?

No → Consider alternative site or development proposal

Yes

2.26   Prepare Level 2 FRA Report

2.27   If appropriate, submit report to LPA/FDA for review[6]

2.28   Undertake Level 3 FRA (Go to Box 3.1 in Flowchart 3)

6.3 LEVEL 3 FLOOD RISK ASSESSMENT

Flowchart 3 provides guidance on the procedures to be followed when undertaking a Level 3 FRA, as part of a tiered three-level approach to flood risk assessment (Section 5.3.2). It is recommended that the reader refers to Section 6.2 before undertaking a Level 3 FRA.

Further details on undertaking a Level 3 FRA can be found in Section 5.3.4 and Appendix A2.3.

3.1   From Box 2.28 of Flowchart 2 (Sheet 3 of 3)

3.2   Refer to Section 5.3.4 and Appendix A2.3

3.3   Collect information required for Level 3 FRA (Box 2.24)

3.4   Undertake analysis to quantify existing flood risks to the site (Appendix A2.3), including climate change allowances (Refer to Box 5.3 in Chapter 5)

3.5.   Based on the above analysis, indicate the flood risk to the site associated with each of the flooding hazards

Flooding hazard	High Risk[5]	Low to Medium Risk[5]	Little or No Risk[5]
Fluvial flooding			
Flooding from the sea			
Flooding from estuaries/tidelocked watercourses			
Groundwater flooding			
Overland flow flooding			
Flooding from artificial drainage systems			
Flooding due to infrastructure failure			

3.6   Based on the above results, and consideration of maintenance access and development runoff, if required, summarise the flood issues which the development will need to be designed to manage

Flooding hazard	Flooding of the development	Increase in upstream flood risk	Increase in downstream flood risk
Fluvial flooding			
Flooding from the sea			
Flooding from estuaries/watercourses affected by tidelocking			
Groundwater flooding			
Overland flow flooding			
Flooding from artificial drainage systems			
Flooding due to infrastructure failure			

Development runoff management
Maintenance access

3.7 Go to Box 3.8 in Flowchart 3 (Sheet 2 of 2)

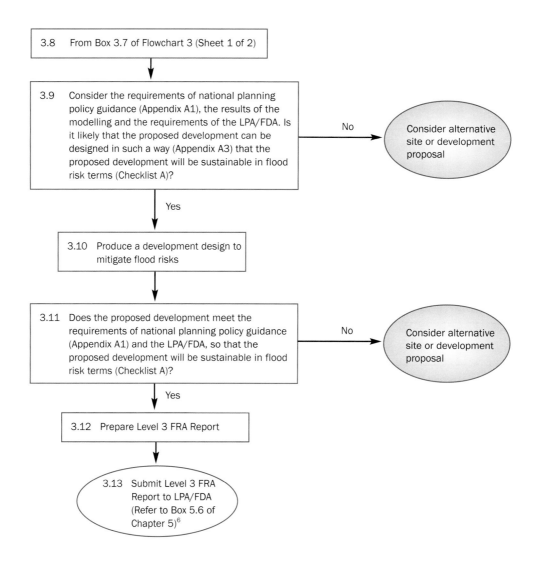

3.8   From Box 3.7 of Flowchart 3 (Sheet 1 of 2)

3.9   Consider the requirements of national planning policy guidance (Appendix A1), the results of the modelling and the requirements of the LPA/FDA. Is it likely that the proposed development can be designed in such a way (Appendix A3) that the proposed development will be sustainable in flood risk terms (Checklist A)?

No → Consider alternative site or development proposal

Yes

3.10   Produce a development design to mitigate flood risks

3.11   Does the proposed development meet the requirements of national planning policy guidance (Appendix A1) and the LPA/FDA, so that the proposed development will be sustainable in flood risk terms (Checklist A)?

No → Consider alternative site or development proposal

Yes

3.12   Prepare Level 3 FRA Report

3.13   Submit Level 3 FRA Report to LPA/FDA (Refer to Box 5.6 of Chapter 5)[6]

Part D

APPENDICES

A1   National arrangements for the control of development and flood risk

Note: This Appendix describes the national arrangements as they existed in March 2004, but they are continually evolving; prospective developers should confirm current requirements with the local planning authority.

A1.1   ENGLAND

A1.1.1   Planning policy

The national planning policy for England in relation to management of flood risk is set out in Planning Policy Guidance Note 25 *Development and Flood Risk*, known as PPG25 (DTLR, 2001). PPG20 (Department of the Environment, 1992) provides complementary guidance in relation to planning in coastal areas. The foreword to PPG25 states:

> "This guidance explains how flood risk should be considered at all stages of the planning and development process in order to reduce future damage to property and loss of life. It sets out the importance the Government attaches to the management and reduction of flood risk in the land-use planning process, to acting on a precautionary basis and to taking account of climate change. It summarises the responsibilities of various parties in the development process. The planning system should ensure that new development is safe and not exposed unnecessarily to flooding by considering flood risk on a catchment-wide basis and, where necessary, across administrative boundaries. It should seek where possible to reduce and certainly not to increase flood risk. It should help ensure that flood plains are used for their natural purposes, continue to function effectively and are protected from inappropriate development. The guidance also outlines how flood risk issues should be addressed in regional planning guidance, development plans and in the consideration of planning applications."

The following section provides brief details of the flood risk zoning approach taken in PPG25 (DTLR, 2001) current in March 2004.

The planning procedures outlined below are based on the planning procedures in England as they existed at March 2004. The planning system in England is undergoing a major phase of reforms. The government produced a Green Paper on the planning system in December 2001 and the Planning and Compulsory Purchase Act is expected to come into effect in 2004. The proposed reforms will predominantly affect the way in which local planning authorities (LPAs) prepare development plans, although some changes are to be made to the planning application system. As part of the reforms all Planning Policy Guidance Notes will be reviewed and reissued as Planning Policy Statements.

Readers are strongly advised to familiarise themselves with the national planning policy guidance by reference to PPG25, or any successor documents that may in future apply.

PPG25 indicates that the government considers that it is important that the planning system effectively addresses the issues of flood-risk management as they affect the development process. In particular, as part of its strategy for sustainable development, the government wishes to avoid an unnecessary increase in the requirement to provide artificial defence against flooding. PPG25 recognises that a sustainable approach to flood risk will involve avoiding additional development in some areas. Where this is not possible, development needs to be of a design and with an appropriate level of protection to ensure that the risk of damage from flooding is minimised, while not increasing the risk of flooding elsewhere. LPAs should, therefore, consider the information available on the nature of flood risk and its potential consequences and accord it appropriate weight in the preparation of development plans and the determination of applications for planning permission.

PPG 25 requires that LPAs should adopt a risk-based approach to proposals for development in or affecting flood-risk areas. The assessment of risk should take account of:

- the area liable to flooding

- the probability of it occurring, both now and over time

- the extent and standard of existing flood defences and their effectiveness over time

- the likely depth of flooding

- the rates of flow likely to be involved

- the likelihood of impacts to other areas, properties and habitats

- the effects of climate change

- the nature and currently expected lifetime of the development proposed and the extent to which it is designed to deal with flood risk.

PPG25 requires LPAs to apply the risk-based approach to the preparation of development plans and their decisions on development control through a sequential test. Developers seeking sites for housing and other development should also have regard to this test.

The sequential test involves giving priority in allocating or permitting sites for development, in descending order, to the flood zones set out in Table 1 of PPG25 (reproduced as Box A1.1 of this guide), including the sub-divisions in Zone 3. These zones are defined in terms of divisions of annual probability of flooding. When allocating land in development plans or deciding applications for development at any particular location, those responsible for the decision would be expected to demonstrate that there are no reasonable options available in a lower-risk category, consistent with other sustainable development objectives. PPG25 notes that it is important also to consider that these zones cover only river, tidal and coastal flooding. Locally in all zones, an assessment may be needed of the risk of groundwater flooding or local flooding due to overland sheet flow or runoff exceeding the capacity of drainage systems during prolonged or intense rainfall. Flood-resistant construction may be required in all areas, depending on the results of that assessment. The runoff implications of development should also be assessed for all zones and controlled, where possible, through the use of sustainable drainage systems.

Box A1.1 *Planning response to sequential characterisation of flood risk* – Table 1 from PPG25 (DTLR, 2001)

Flood Zone (see Note a)	Appropriate planning response
1 Little or no risk Annual probability of flooding: River, tidal & coastal <0.1%	No constraints due to river, tidal or coastal flooding.
2 Low to medium risk Annual probability of flooding: River 0.1-1.0% Tidal & coastal 0.1-0.5%	Suitable for most development. For this and higher-risk zones, flood risk assessment appropriate to the scale and nature of the development and the risk should be provided with applications or at time of local plan allocation. Flood-resistant construction and suitable warning/evacuation procedures may be required depending on the flood risk assessment. Subject to operational requirements in terms of response times, these and the higher-risk zones below are generally not suitable for essential civil infrastructure, such as hospitals, fire stations, emergency depots etc. Where such infrastructure has to be, or is already, located in these areas, access must be guaranteed and they must be capable of remaining operational in times of emergency due to extreme flooding.
3 High risk (see note b) Annual probability of flooding, with defences where they exist: River 1.0% or greater Tidal & coastal 0.5% or greater	**a. Developed areas** These areas may be suitable for residential, commercial and industrial development provided the appropriate minimum standard of flood defence (including suitable warning and evacuation procedures) can be maintained for the lifetime of the development (see paragraph 31 of PPG25). Preference must be given to those areas already defended to that standard. In allocating or permitting sites for development, authorities should seek to avoid areas that will be needed, or have significant potential, for coastal managed realignment or washland creation as part of the overall flood defence strategy for coastal cells and river catchments. **b. Undeveloped and sparsely developed areas** These areas are generally not suitable for residential, commercial and industrial development unless a particular location is essential, eg for navigation and water-based recreation uses, agriculture and essential transport and utilities infrastructure, and an alternative lower-risk location is not available. General-purpose housing or other development comprising residential or institutional accommodation should not normally be permitted. Residential uses should be limited to job-related accommodation (eg caretakers and operational staff). Caravan and camping sites should generally not be located in these areas. Where, exceptionally, development is permitted, it should be provided with the appropriate minimum standard of flood defence and should not impede flood flows or result in a net loss of flood-plain storage. **c. Functional flood plains** These areas may be suitable for some recreation, sport, amenity and conservation uses (provided adequate warning and evacuation procedures are in place). Built development should be wholly exceptional and limited to essential transport and utilities infrastructure that has to be there. Such infrastructure should be designed and constructed to remain operational even at times of flood, to result in no net loss of flood-plain storage, not to impede water flows and not to increase flood risk elsewhere. There should be a presumption against the provision of camping and caravan sites.

Notes:

(a) All risks relate to the time at which a land allocation decision is made or an application submitted. The Environment Agency will publish maps of these flood zones. Flood zones should be identified from Environment Agency flood data ignoring the presence of flood defences. Local planning authorities should, with the Environment Agency, identify those areas currently protected by defences and the standard of protection provided by those defences.

(b) Development should not be permitted where existing sea or river defences, properly maintained, would not provide an acceptable standard of safety over the lifetime of the development, as such land would be extremely vulnerable should a flood defence embankment or sea wall be breached, in particular because of the speed of flooding in such circumstances.

PPG25 requires that, in applying the sequential test, local planning authorities should consult and take the advice from the Environment Agency on the distribution of flood risk and the availability of flood defences in their areas. They should take account of the resulting level of actual risk in drawing up development plans and policies and considering proposals and applications for development. This test should also take into account the effects of flood risk on both local public transport availability and the surrounding road network serving any proposed development. Where extensive areas of land fall into the high-risk zones, further development may be needed to avoid social and economic stagnation or blight, or to allow existing development to be adequately protected. Where, in the wider overall interest, permission is granted exceptionally for development within an undeveloped or sparsely developed flood plain, the threat of flooding should be managed to ensure that the development is, and remains, safe throughout its lifetime and does not increase flood risk elsewhere.

PPG25 states that flood defences for most new housing development should be designed and constructed to protect against the flood with an annual probability of 1 per cent for river flooding and 0.5 per cent for coastal flooding for a period of 50 years, taking into account the allowances for climate change contained in the Project Appraisal Guidance for flood and coastal defence cited in Appendix A of PPG25. Commercial and industrial development should aim to achieve the same minimum standard of defence. Where necessary, conditions should be attached to permissions and/or agreements used to secure these objectives.

PPG25 notes that the insurance industry has become increasingly concerned about flood risks, and the scale of the resulting claims. Before insurance is offered, some companies are using increasingly sophisticated techniques to identify the risk to specific properties. Developments at risk of flooding may face increasing difficulties with the cost or availability of insurance and this, in turn, could cause problems for property buyers in obtaining mortgages. In extreme cases, properties might remain unsold, leading to blight on the whole development. **Developers are advised, therefore, to seek the views of insurers at an early stage.** For its own part, the insurance industry may wish to seek to reduce the risk exposure by making appropriate representations about proposals for the location of new development during the preparation of development plans. Authorities should consider consulting their own insurers to ensure that flood defence or other measures are adequate and are likely to satisfy the requirements of insurers.

For certain types of project, environmental impact assessments are required and developers are advised to contact the LPA to determine whether such an assessment will be needed and, if so, what it should cover.

A1.1.2 Flood defence agencies

Similar arrangements for flood defence agencies (FDAs) exist in England and Wales. This section is relevant to both countries.

For most development proposals within England and Wales the principal FDA to be consulted with regard to planning applications will be the Environment Agency. However, in certain circumstances internal drainage boards and local authorities can also act as the FDA, and may also be consulted. These bodies are described below.

Environment Agency

The principal aim of the Environment Agency, as stated in the Environment Act 1995 and summarised in PPG25, is to contribute towards the achievement of sustainable development. Within its wide-ranging responsibilities, the Environment Agency has a duty to exercise a general supervision over all matters relating to flood defence in England and Wales. Under Section 105 of the Water Resources Act 1991, the Environment Agency was required to carry out surveys relating to flood defence, and the resulting documents are generally referred to as "Section 105 Surveys". The Environment Agency has also produced the indicative flood plain maps referred to in Appendix A2.1.1. While these surveys and maps are to be updated "from time to time", the Environment Agency has a continual programme of recording and archiving hydrometric data, including river levels and flows, groundwater levels and water quality information. The Environment Agency is developing a range of management plans covering its flood defence, water resources, pollution control and fisheries functions and environmental duties. These surveys, records and plans can provide valuable information for use in flood risk assessments.

The Environment Agency has permissive powers to maintain and improve watercourses and flood defence works and to construct new works. However, except where the powers are to be used for defence against the sea or tidal water, the use of these powers is restricted to lengths of watercourse designated "main river". This refers to formal designation on a main river map maintained by the Department of Environment, Food and Rural Affairs (Defra), and watercourses which are not so designated are known as "ordinary watercourses". The EA's powers are permissive not mandatory, and improvement works are programmed on a priority basis. In particular, **the Environment Agency does not promote, at public expense, schemes to protect new development from flooding unless this is incidental to the reduction of flood risk to existing properties.** The EA has certain rights to enter land, and to deposit dredged material on land next to a watercourse.

The Environment Agency operates flood forecasting and warning procedures for many areas at risk of flooding, throughout England and Wales, and the related documentation can be an additional source of information for FRAs.

The Environment Agency is a statutory consultee when Structure Plans and Part 1 Unitary Development Plans (UDPs) are being prepared, and will also contribute to the preparation of Local Plans and Part 2 UDPs. The Environment Agency will normally be consulted by an LPA regarding any application for planning permission where flood risk is likely to be a material consideration. At an earlier stage, Environment Agency staff may be able to indicate the general requirements that would have to be met to avoid or manage flood risks. It is the responsibility of the developer to investigate whether, and if so how, the EA's objectives can be achieved in a way that will be acceptable to the planning authority, the Environment Agency and any other relevant FDAs such as an internal drainage board or local authority.

The Environment Agency has produced Standing Advice (Environment Agency, 2003b) to enable LPAs to make decisions on low risk planning applications where flood risk is an issue without directly consulting the Agency for an individual response. In addition to a General Guidance Note for LPA's, the Standing Advice comprises:

- maps showing the indicative location and extent of flood risk areas

- a Flood Risk Response Matrix as a spreadsheet in Excel® (the "matrix")

- a series of four technical guidance notes on flood risk assessment for different types of development in different locations.

The "matrix" identifies situations where the risk is sufficiently low such that direct consultation with the FDA is not required, and situations where consultation with the FDA should be undertaken. If a site is located in an area where direct consultation with the Environment Agency is not required, the information given in the Standing Advice should be treated as if it were advice provided by the Environment Agency via a direct consultation response.

Internal drainage boards

Certain areas of England and Wales are designated internal drainage districts (IDDs). For each such district, an internal drainage board (IDB) has permissive flood defence powers and duties in relation to ordinary watercourses within the district. On request, the LPA or the Environment Agency will be able to indicate whether the site of a proposed development is in an IDD. If this is the case, the IDB should be consulted in addition to the Environment Agency as they often have detailed local information regarding flood risk. An IDB's powers to maintain and improve ordinary watercourses and related flood defence works, and to construct new works, are generally the equivalent of the EA's powers in relation to main river. The policy of IDBs regarding the protection of proposed development from flooding is similar to that of the Environment Agency.

Local authorities

Local authorities have some permissive flood defence powers in relation to ordinary watercourses outside IDDs. However, their powers to maintain and improve watercourses and flood defence works, and to construct new works at public expense, are limited to work which may be necessary for the purpose of preventing flooding or mitigating any damage caused by flooding. Also, a local authority shall not carry out or maintain any drainage works except with the consent of, and in accordance with any reasonable conditions imposed by, the Environment Agency. Nevertheless, local authorities often have very useful information regarding flood risks associated with some, if not all, the ordinary watercourses in their area.

A1.1.3 Additional consents

The Environment Agency has regulatory powers to control proposed works which would affect watercourses or flood defences, including any proposals for work within prescribed distances of watercourses and flood defences. These powers derive from the Land Drainage Act 1991, the Water Resources Act 1991 and bye-laws adopted by the Environment Agency. While some of the powers relate only to watercourses designated as a main river, others apply to all watercourses (subject to some powers within internal drainage districts being exercised by internal drainage boards). Additional consents or licences may be required in respect of any proposal to impound water in a watercourse, to abstract water from, or discharge water or trade or sewage effluent to a watercourse or underground strata. The area office of the Environment Agency, local to the site, should be contacted for advice about the formal consents and licences required under any of these powers, and for details of the application procedure.

IDBs have bye-laws relating to ordinary watercourses in their districts. These require consent to be obtained for any works in, or within a prescribed distance of, such a watercourse or flood bank. Some IDBs have bye-laws controlling developments in flood plains and restricting the introduction of additional runoff into IDDs.

Any necessary consents must be obtained, from the Environment Agency or the relevant IDB as appropriate, before any work is carried out on site. This requirement is to ensure that any conditions which may be attached to a consent are complied with from the start of the work on site.

A1.2   WALES

A1.2.1   Planning policy

The current national planning policy for Wales in relation to management of flood risk is set out in the Welsh Assembly document "Planning Policy Wales Chapter 13 – Minimising and Managing Environmental Risks and Pollution" (National Assembly for Wales, 2002) and the associated Technical Advice Note (Wales) 15 issued in March 1998 (National Assembly for Wales, 1998). A draft updated version of the latter document, Technical Advice Note (Wales) 15 *Development and Flood Risk* (National Assembly for Wales, 2003a) was issued as a Consultation Draft in July 2003, followed by a Corrigenda in September 2003 (National Assembly for Wales, 2003b). The introduction to this Consultation Draft, referred to below as TAN15 states:

> "This TAN provides technical guidance which supplements the policy set out in Planning Policy Wales (PPW) in relation to development and flooding. It advises on development and flood risk as this relates to sustainability principles (Section 2.2 PPW), and provides a methodology against which risks arising from both river and coastal flooding, and from additional runoff from development, in any location, can be assessed".

The following section provides brief details of the flood risk zoning approach taken in TAN15. It should be noted that at the time of preparation of this guide TAN15 is in draft format, and the information provided in this Appendix is therefore likely to be subject to some change. Readers are strongly advised to familiarise themselves with the national planning policy guidance by reference to the latest version of TAN15, or any successor documents that may apply in the future.

TAN15 recognises that, historically, the topography of Wales has generally resulted in transport infrastructure and development in Wales being concentrated on valley floors, lowland areas and in the coastal fringes. A large proportion of the Welsh population is located within urban centres along the coastal plain in North and South Wales, particularly Cardiff, Swansea and Newport and the coastal settlements of North Wales.

TAN15 indicates that the incidence and extent of both river and coastal flooding should be expected to increase with time as a consequence of changes in hydrological conditions and human activity and climate change. New development must be planned sensibly, including consideration of climate change.

The general approach of PPW and TAN15 is to advise caution in respect of new development in areas at risk of flooding. The overarching aim is to direct new development away from those areas which are at high risk of flooding. The precautionary methodology seeks to achieve this by adopting a two-stage test in high risk areas:

1   Development in flood risk areas requires strong justification. It will be necessary to ensure that most new development is directed away from flood risk areas and ensure that only those developments which can be justified on the basis of specific criteria (see Section 8 of TAN15) are located within high risk areas.

2   In order to determine the acceptability of all development in flood risk areas an assessment of flooding consequences will be required. It will be necessary to determine the consequences for people and property of developing in flood risk areas before deciding whether those consequences are acceptable and can be acceptably managed (see Section 9 and Appendix 1 of TAN15). Where the risks and consequences of flooding cannot be managed to an acceptable level then developing in these areas shall be avoided irrespective of other criteria.

TAN15 states that, in addition to adhering to the precautionary principle, planning authorities should recognise that flooding from surface water runoff, if not properly controlled, can result in flooding at other locations.

TAN15 includes "planning maps" which, based on the best currently available information, show the extent of the flood risk zones described in a table in TAN15 (reproduced in this guide as Box A1.2). These maps are at present based on a variety of sources, and they will be refined as more information becomes available. Showing the extent of the zones on maps in the national guidance is an alternative to specifying the extent of the zones in probability terms and requiring LPAs to produce the maps.

The planning maps differentiate between three zones of differing levels of flood risk:

A: Little or no risk.

B: Low to medium risk.

C: High risk, subdivided into C1 defended and C2 undefended areas.

TAN15 indicates that the planning maps are based on the best available information on flood risk. The maps have been agreed between the National Assembly for Wales and the Environment Agency for planning purposes associated with the use of TAN15. While robust for current assessments (both forward planning and decision making), the planning maps are expected to be refined over time. Future versions of the maps are likely to be issued as numbered and dated copies which will supersede earlier versions.

Box A1.2 *Risk zones from TAN15* (National Assembly for Wales, 2003a,b)[1]

	Zone	Advice	Requirements
A	Little or no risk	No constraints relating to river or coastal flooding, other than to avoid increasing risk elsewhere	Refer to section 10 of TAN15. Use of SUDS to be encouraged
B	Low–Medium risk	Generally suitable for most forms of development. Assessments, where required, are unlikely to identify consequences that cannot be overcome or managed to an acceptable level. It is unlikely, therefore, that these would result in a refusal of planning consent on the grounds of flooding. Refer to Section 9 and Appendix 1 of TAN15	Where flood risk identified as a material consideration proposals to be subject to Section 9 and Appendix 1 The extent of assessment to be related to scale and nature of proposal and to be determined by the planning authority with assistance from Environment Agency or other appropriate body. Appendix 1 of TAN15 Use of SUDS to be encouraged.
C	High risk C1 **Defended**	Requirement for UDP allocations and applications for all built development to be justified in accordance with Section 8 and to be considered acceptable in accordance with Section 9 and Appendix 1 of TAN15	Statement demonstrating requirements of Section 8 have been satisfied, or can be satisfied, to be included in UDP. Refer to paragraphs 16.2 –16.4 Flood consequences assessment required in accordance with Section 9 and Appendix 1 of TAN15 before UDP allocation Statement demonstrating requirements of Section 8 have been satisfied, or can be satisfied, to accompany planning application. Refer to paragraphs 17.2 and 17.4 Flood consequences assessment required for planning applications in accordance with Section 9 and Appendix 1 of TAN15. Information to accompany planning application, paragraph 17.3 In such cases, any improvements to flood defences must first be approved by the appropriate operating authority and mechanisms for long term maintenance agreements in place refer to paragraph 21.1 – 21.3
	High risk C2 **Undefended**	The flooding consequences associated with emergency services and highly vulnerable built development are not considered to be acceptable. UDP allocations should not be made for such development and planning applications not proposed UDP allocations or applications for less vulnerable built development to be justified in accordance with Section 8 and to be considered acceptable in accordance with Section 9 and Appendix 1 of TAN15	Highly Vulnerable built development and Emergency Services will not be permitted Flood consequences assessment required in accordance with Section 9 and Appendix 1 before UDP allocation Statement demonstrating requirements of section 8 have been satisfied, or can be satisfied, paragraphs 18.2 and 18.4 Flood consequences assessment required for planning applications in accordance with Section 9 and Appendix 1. Information to accompany planning application, paragraph 18.3 In such cases, adequate flood defences must first be approved by the appropriate operating authority and mechanisms for long term maintenance agreements etc in place refer to paragraphs 21.1-3

[1] The references to all sections, appendices and paragraph numbers given in this table refer to those of the TAN15 document. It is recommended that the reader refers to TAN15.

Zone C represents the flood plain, all of which is a high risk area, subdivided into two different zones on the basis of information supplied by the Environment Agency.

Zone C1 is defined as a high risk area, which benefits from some form of nominal engineered flood protection against floods with an annual probability of occurrence of 2 per cent or higher. However, it must be recognised that the presence of protection measures does not eliminate risk completely and that certain developments are defined in TAN15 as more vulnerable than others and so require higher degrees of protection. Indeed, should the defences be overtopped or breached, then the consequences of flooding, particularly in the immediate proximity to the breach, may well be significant.

Zone C2 is defined as a high risk area not benefiting from the flood defence protection attributed to zone C1. It includes those parts of the active flood plain where development would interfere with natural and man-made washlands and restrict the storage of floodwaters during flood events.

Zone B represents areas of medium to low flood risk which lie outside zone C and extend to the limits of the extreme flood outline. The Environment Agency plans to model the extreme flood outlines for England and Wales as part of its flood mapping strategy. It is intended that this extreme outline will be used to prepare the guidance maps in due course. In the interim this boundary is represented by river terraces 1 and 2 mapped by the British Geological Survey (BGS).

Zone A is defined as the area of little or no risk and represents all areas outside the extreme flood outline. However, flooding is not confined to flood plains and heavy rain falling on waterlogged ground can cause localised flooding almost anywhere. Runoff from developments in these areas can, if not properly controlled, result in flooding at other locations and significantly alter the frequency and extent of floods further down the catchment.

TAN15 requires that new development should be directed away from zone C and towards zones A or B (preferably zone A), where river or coastal flooding will be less of an issue. In zone C the tests outlined in Sections 8 and 9 of TAN15 will be applied, recognising, however, that highly vulnerable built development in undefended areas (zone C2) should not be permitted.

TAN15 emphasises that any development in flood risk areas requires strong justification, but it recognises that there are circumstances where certain developments can be approved if the consequences of flooding are acceptable for the type of development proposed. The document includes guidance on the assessment of the consequences of flooding and the acceptability of such consequences.

Particular flooding consequences may not be acceptable for particular types of development. The precautionary methodology identifies the vulnerability of different land uses to flooding, and for this purpose, TAN15 sub-divides built development into three categories shown in Box A1.3.

Box A1.3   *Categories of built development from TAN15 (National Assembly for Wales, 2003a)*

Built development category	Definition
Emergency services	Hospitals; ambulance, fire, police and coastguard stations; command centres, emergency depots and buildings used to provide emergency shelter in time of flood
Highly vulnerable built development	All residential premises (including hotels and caravan parks), public buildings (eg schools, libraries, leisure centres), especially vulnerable industrial development (eg power stations, chemical plants, incinerators) and waste disposal sites
Less vulnerable built development	General industrial, employment, commercial and retail development, transport and utilities infrastructure, mineral extraction sites and associated processing facilities, excluding waste disposal sites

TAN15 indicates that highly vulnerable development and emergency services should not be permitted in zone C2. All other new development should only be permitted within zones C1 and C2 if determined by the LPA to be justified in that location. It is considered perfectly reasonable for planning authorities to require all development permitted in high risk areas (zone C), including those already granted outline permission, to plan for the consequences of flooding.

The approach outlined in TAN15 encourages applicants to accept that the risk of flooding will always be a material consideration in zone C. However, it should be remembered that flooding may be an issue in all zones. In preparing proposals for development, applicants should discuss, with the LPA, the requirements they will be expected to meet to satisfy the LPA, with reference to the advice in the TAN15.

TAN15 indicates that developers should approach the Environment Agency for advice on the potential consequences of flooding to their proposed development before undertaking assessment of flooding consequences. The Environment Agency will provide advice on the scope of the assessment needed commensurate with the nature and scale of the proposed development.

TAN15 indicates that, when an LPA receives a planning application which is within flood zone B or C, it should undertake appropriate internal consultation in relation to its own flood defence responsibilities as well as consulting the Environment Agency. Local planning authorities should also, where relevant, consult with internal drainage boards on developments within internal drainage districts and outside where it would have an impact in them. The Environment Agency, or any other relevant bodies, should provide advice to the LPA on the findings and conclusions of the assessment of flood consequences, including the impact on flooding elsewhere or the impact of flood alleviation works on other property or nature conservation interest.

Where runoff considerations are likely to be significant, LPAs should undertake appropriate consultation. This will include appropriate internal consultation in relation to their own flood defence responsibilities, the Environment Agency, the sewerage undertaker and, where relevant, any navigation authority on the capacity of existing drainage systems.

TAN 15 notes that an environmental impact assessment may be required for some proposals and developers are advised to contact the LPA to determine whether such an assessment will be needed and, if so, what it should cover.

A1.2.2 Flood defence agencies

Similar arrangements for flood defence agencies exist in England and Wales, see Section A1.1.2.

A1.2.3 Additional consents

Similar arrangements exist in England and Wales, see Section A1.1.3.

A1.3 SCOTLAND

A1.3.1 Planning policy

The national planning policy for Scotland in relation to management of flood risk is set out in National Planning Policy Guideline NPPG7 (Scottish Office, 1995). An updated document Scottish Planning Policy SPP7: *Planning and Flooding* (Scottish Executive, 2004) was issued by the Scottish Executive in February 2004. The summary to SPP7 states:

"Flooding damages property and lives. Many parts of Scotland have a legacy of development at risk of flooding from watercourses, the sea, groundwater and inadequate drainage. Climate change is predicted to worsen the situation. The Scottish Executive expects developers and planning authorities to err on the side of caution in decision-making whenever flooding is an issue. Flood risk will be a material consideration in a range of cases.

New development should not take place if it would be at significant risk of flooding from any source or would materially increase the probability of flooding elsewhere. The storage capacity of functional floodplains should be safeguarded, and works to elevate the level of a site by landraising should not lead to a loss of flood water storage capacity."

Where built up areas already benefit from flood defences, redevelopment of brownfield sites should be acceptable but greenfield proposals will extend the area of built development at risk and should preferably be considered in the light of alternatives through the development plan process. Water-resistant materials and forms of construction may be required. Generally, drainage will be a material consideration and the means of draining a development should be assessed. Sustainable drainage will be required whenever practicable and watercourses should not be culverted. Flood prevention and alleviation measures should respect the wider environmental concerns, and appropriate engineering solutions recognise the context provided by the development plan. While it is preferable for open spaces to flood rather than buildings it may not always be acceptable.

The following section provides brief details of the flood risk zoning approach taken in SPP7 (Scottish Executive, 2004). Readers are strongly advised to familiarise themselves with the national planning policy guidance by reference to the latest version of SPP7, or any successor documents that may apply in the future.

SPP7 states that Scotland already has many properties at risk of flooding. Numerous settlements on flood plains and near the coast have experienced intermittent flooding. In some places the problem has been made worse by inadequate culverts and flood defence measures, runoff from development, and rising groundwater, including changes in the water table due to the cessation of mine pumping. These sources of flooding are not restricted to the flood plain. Flooding from artificial drainage systems is also a problem.

SPP7 states that coastal flooding is not widespread in Scotland but may be expected to increase as a result of climate change. An estimated 90 000 properties have been identified as potentially at risk. More storms and tidal surges are predicted and, together with a rise in sea level, are likely to increase the probability of flooding along the coast.

SPP7 states that the primary responsibility for safeguarding and insuring land or property against natural hazards, such as flooding, lies with the owner. Councils have a range of responsibilities alongside land use planning, including emergency planning, building standards and roads, as well as a duty to maintain watercourses and powers to promote flood prevention schemes (for non-agricultural land). For agricultural and forestry land the owners are responsible for flood defence. Scottish Water has responsibility for the public drainage system, including rain or storm water drains, though road drainage for adopted roads is the responsibility of the roads authority. Property owners are responsible for the private sewers and drains within their curtilage. SEPA operates flood warning systems, and gives advice to local planning authorities on the probability of flooding and flood risk based on the information it holds. British Waterways is responsible for the canal system.

CIRIA C624

SPP7 states that the possibility of flooding from all causes must be given serious consideration by developers and planning authorities, and not merely for sites on the flood plain or in coastal areas. New development should not take place if it would be at significant risk of flooding or increase the probability of flooding elsewhere. New development should not add to the area of land which requires protection by flood prevention measures or compromise major options for flood risk management.

For coastal and watercourse flooding, SPP7 uses a risk-based approach to characterise areas for planning purposes by their annual probability of flooding. The planning response for each flood zone is given in Box A1.4, which reproduces the Risk Framework from SPP7 (Scottish Executive, 2004).

Box A1.4 *The risk framework – The planning response to flood risk (Coastal, tidal and watercourse) from SPP7 (Scottish Executive, 2004)*

---

1. Little or no risk area

Annual probability of watercourse, tidal or coastal flooding: less than 0.1 per cent (1-in-1000). (ie less frequently than the so-called 1-in-1000 year flood)

Appropriate planning response

No constraints due to watercourse, tidal or coastal flooding.

2. Low to medium risk area

Annual probability of watercourse, tidal or coastal flooding: in the range 0.1–0.5 per cent (1-in-1000 – 1-in-200)

Appropriate planning response

It will not usually be necessary to consider flood risk unless local conditions indicate otherwise. Suitable for most development. A flood risk assessment may be required at the upper end of the probability range (ie close to 0.5 per cent) or where the nature of the development or local circumstances indicate heightened risk. Water-resistant materials and construction may be required depending on the flood risk assessment. Subject to operational requirements, including response times, these areas are generally not suitable for essential civil infrastructure, such as hospitals, fire stations, emergency depots etc. Where such infrastructure has to be located in these areas or is being substantially extended, they must be capable of remaining operational and accessible during extreme flooding events.

3. High risk area (see the 2 sub areas below)

Annual probability of watercourse, tidal or coastal flooding: greater than 0.5 per cent (1-in-200)
Generally not suitable for essential civil infrastructure, such as hospitals, fire stations, emergency depots etc schools, ground based electrical and telecommunications equipment. The policy for development on functional flood plains applies. Land raising may be acceptable.

3(a) Within areas already built-up

Appropriate planning response

These areas may be suitable for residential, institutional, commercial and industrial development provided flood prevention measures to the appropriate standard already exist, are under construction or are planned as part of a long term development strategy in a structure plan context. In allocating sites preference should be given to those areas already defended to that standard. Water resistant materials and construction as appropriate.

3(b) Undeveloped and sparsely developed areas

Appropriate planning response

These areas are generally not suitable for additional development, including residential, institutional, commercial and industrial development. Exceptions may arise if a location is essential for operational reasons, e.g. for navigation and water-based recreation uses, agriculture, transport or some utilities infrastructure, and an alternative lower risk location is not achievable. Such infrastructure should be designed and constructed to remain operational during floods. These areas may also be suitable for some recreation, sport, amenity and nature conservation uses (provided adequate evacuation procedures are in place). Job-related accommodation (eg caretakers and operational staff) may be acceptable. New caravan and camping sites should generally not be located in these areas. Exceptionally, if built development is permitted, flood prevention and alleviation measures are likely to be required and the loss of storage capacity minimised. Water resistant materials and construction as appropriate. Land should not be developed if it will be needed or have significant potential for coastal managed realignment or washland creation as part of an overall flood defence.

For notes (see next page)

Notes on the risk framework

(a) The annual probabilities relate to the land at the time an application is submitted or a land allocation is made.

(b) In the longer-term the calculated probabilities of flooding may be affected by climate change, improved data/methods and land uses elsewhere in the catchment.

(c) As paragraph 33 explains this framework necessarily simplifies the situation.

The SPP7 Risk Framework is based on the consideration that for planning purposes it is reasonable on present evidence to regard areas with an annual probability of river or coastal flooding of 0.5 per cent or above to be characterised as at high risk of flooding. Based on current predictions this figure includes an allowance for climate change but freeboard (ie the height above a predicted flood level which is needed to take account of any waves or turbulence) will be additional. The Scottish Executive also considers that the outer limit to the area of concern for extreme flood events may be defined by an annual probability of flooding of 0.1 per cent including climate change.

SPP7 notes that the calculated probability of a flood occurring should be regarded as a best estimate and not a precise forecast. Developers and local planning authorities should therefore err on the side of caution in taking decisions when flood risk is an issue.

SPP7 states that developers should use pre-application discussions (such as with the LPA and SEPA) to help identify if flooding is an issue. Developers should commission a flood risk assessment and/or a drainage assessment immediately a potential flooding issue is identified. This information may prevent abortive expenditure, will clarify the situation and, if the site is developable in principle, it ought to give advice on the need for any alleviation measures. Planning authorities have powers to require an assessment. This is applicable to outline as well as full applications.

SPP7 states that LPAs are required to consult SEPA before granting planning permission where it appears to them that the development is likely to result in a material increase in the number of buildings at risk of being damaged by flooding. SEPA have issued planning authorities with indicative flood risk maps.

SPP7 notes that insurers are concerned about flood risk and the level of potential resultant claims. Insurers have stated that it is their intention to continue to provide flood insurance in as many existing cases as possible, but new development in areas at risk of flooding which lack adequate protection may face difficulty in obtaining cover, or may face significantly increased premiums. In turn, this may affect the availability of mortgages, possibly affecting the viability of development. Developers should consider the availability of insurance for subsequent purchasers or tenants at an early stage in their evaluation of the site.

SPP7 notes that flood prevention and alleviation measures should not lead to a deterioration in the ecological status of the water environment, and may provide opportunities for habitat enhancement or creation. The environmental policies of the development plan will provide the context for considering appropriate engineering solutions.

Other documents which provide relevant guidance include Planning Advice Note PAN61 (Scottish Executive, 2001), which relates to planning and SUDS, and the final report of the Committee of Scottish Local Authorities (COSLA) Flooding Task Group (COSLA, 2003). This document discusses the responsibilities of the various bodies concerned with planning and flood risk and, among many other points, recognises that councils, as planning authorities, must find a balance between acceptable flood risk and the need to facilitate development and regeneration. It also draws attention to the fact that "where a council is minded to grant consent against the advice of SEPA, the Scottish Executive must be notified, and this may result in the application being called in" (Section 4.4.2).

A1.3.2   Flood defence agencies

Within Scotland, both SEPA and local authorities have responsibilities for flood defence and may be consulted about proposed developments. The duties of the various bodies concerned with planning and flood risk have been clarified by COSLA (2003).

Scottish Environment Protection Agency

The principal aim of SEPA is to provide an efficient and integrated environmental protection system for Scotland that will both improve the environment and contribute to the Scottish ministers' goal of sustainable development.

A specific function of SEPA under the Environment Act 1995 is to assess, as far as it considers it appropriate, the risk of flooding in any area of Scotland. If requested by a LPA, SEPA will, on the basis of such information as it holds, provide the LPA with advice about the risk of flooding in any part of the LPA's area. SEPA has provided LPAs with indicative flood risk maps which provide a starting point for the identification of areas which are unsuitable for various types of development on flood risk grounds, and it is intended that these maps will be updated to provide more detailed information on flood risk. SEPA advice is available to LPAs in connection with the preparation of development plans, and in relation to individual planning applications where the LPA identifies flood risk as a potential material consideration. The SEPA advice may include recommendations regarding the need for, and the scope of, an FRA and the objectives of any necessary mitigation measures.

SEPA also collects and archives hydrometric data from sites throughout Scotland, and operates flood forecasting and warning procedures for many areas at risk of flooding. SEPA may therefore hold much valuable information relevant to an FRA, and prospective developers are advised to consult the local office of SEPA at an early stage in considering any site.

SEPA does not have permissive powers to maintain and improve watercourses, or to construct new works for flood defence.

Local authorities

Local authorities in Scotland have permissive powers under the Flood Prevention (Scotland) Act 1961 to maintain watercourses and flood defences, to operate any flood defence apparatus, and to provide new flood defences, provided the purpose is to prevent or mitigate flooding of non-agricultural land. However, any flood prevention operations other than maintenance and management operations, (ie generally, the construction of any new works) can be carried out only in accordance with a flood prevention scheme approved by the Scottish Executive. Such schemes are normally aimed at reducing flood risk to existing properties.

The Flood Prevention and Land Drainage (Scotland) Act 1997 requires local authorities to ascertain whether any watercourse in their area is in a condition which is likely to cause flooding of non-agricultural land. Where any watercourse is found to be in such a condition, and it appears to the authority that the exercise of its maintenance powers would substantially reduce the likelihood of such flooding, the Local Authority is, in most cases, required to exercise those powers. The maintenance powers referred to are those defined in Section 2(1)(a) of the Flood Prevention (Scotland) Act 1961. Every two years, each local authority is required to report on occurrences of flooding of non-agricultural land since the previous report, the action it has taken, and the action it still needs to take, to prevent or mitigate flooding of such land.

Local authorities may therefore have detailed information relating to watercourses in their areas which may supplement advice from SEPA.

A1.3.3 Additional consents

SEPA's wide range of environmental responsibilities includes the control of discharges to the water environment through a licensing and monitoring system. SEPA provides guidance regarding any proposed works in watercourses but, at the time of writing, does not have any powers for directly controlling physical works in or next to watercourses (except as regards any pollution risks). This may change in the foreseeable future.

Prospective developers should check the need for discharge or other consents, and seek guidance regarding any work which might be required in a watercourse, when they contact SEPA regarding the availability of information relating to flood risk.

A1.4 NORTHERN IRELAND

A1.4.1 Planning policy

At the time of writing of this guide, no national planning policy for Northern Ireland in relation to management of flood risk has been issued. It is however anticipated that a draft Planning Policy Statement 15 Planning and Flood Risk, known as PPS15, will be issued for consultation in 2004. It is expected that the approach to be adopted will, in principle, be consistent with the risk-based flood zoning methodology applicable in the rest of the United Kingdom.

Although no national planning policy exists for Northern Ireland, flood risk is still a material consideration in the planning process. When the Planning Service considers that flood risk is relevant to a site a flood risk assessment is likely to be required. The Planning Service may also consult with the Rivers Agency and other FDAs.

Readers are strongly advised to discuss the requirements for the assessment of flood risk with the Planning Service and the Rivers Agency and to familiarise themselves with the any national planning policy guidance, including PPS15, or any successor documents that may apply in the future.

A1.4.2 Flood defence agencies

Rivers Agency

The Rivers Agency (RA) is an Executive Agency within the Department of Agriculture and Rural Development. The principal aims of the RA are to improve social conditions and to support economic development by:

- reducing risk to life and damage to property as a result of flooding from rivers and the sea
- preserving the productive potential of agricultural land.

The RA has discretionary powers to maintain more than 6800 km of designated watercourses and 26 km of designated sea defences. Decisions on which watercourses and sea defences are designated are taken by the Drainage Council for Northern Ireland. The Council is an independent body which has responsibility for overseeing the programme for publicly-funded drainage and flood defence schemes in Northern Ireland. The criteria for designation are that the benefits to society as a whole from any improvement works should exceed the cost of the works, and that the required works cannot reasonably be undertaken by riparian owners. The RA is responsible for identifying, designing and executing capital works in approved programmes, with due regard to environmental issues and procedures.

The RA operates the Northern Ireland surface water hydrometric network which provides data on river flows. Technical advice is provided to the Planning Service of Northern Ireland with regard to the drainage aspects of area plan proposals and individual planning applications. The RA has ongoing liaison with the Planning Service in relation to the drainage implications arising from the zoning of new land for housing or industrial development. The necessary drainage infrastructure works to facilitate development will be provided where they meet required financial and sustainability criteria.

A1.4.3 Additional consents

The following is only a brief summary of the situation in March 2004, and prospective developers should check the detailed requirements with the Departments concerned.

Pollution prevention

Section 9 of the Water (Northern Ireland) Order 1999 prescribes that the consent of the Department of the Environment is required for any discharge of trade or sewage effluent to any watercourse or to underground strata. The relevant consent procedure is operated by the Environment and Heritage Service of the Department of the Environment in Northern Ireland.

Drainage and flood defence

Schedule 6 of the Drainage (Northern Ireland) Order 1973 prescribes a list of activities that must not be undertaken without the consent of "the Ministry" (now the Department of Agriculture and Rural Development). The list includes, generally, works in, over or under any watercourse, works which could interfere with the maintenance of a watercourse, and works that could impair the efficiency of sea defences. The relevant consent procedure is operated by the Rivers Agency.

A2   Technical guidance on flood risk assessment

This Appendix provides guidance on the technical aspects of flood risk assessment. It provides an introduction to the issues that are relevant to specific flooding mechanisms, and guidance on where relevant data may be found and the types of techniques that may be employed within FRAs. It is not intended to be a detailed specification of techniques, as it is recommended that FRAs should be carried out under the direction of a qualified and competent person (Appendix A4).

The structure of this Appendix is based on the tiered three-level approach to FRA (Section 5.3). Appendix A2.1 provides guidance on undertaking a Level 1 FRA. Appendices A2.2 and A2.3 provide guidance on Level 2 and Level 3 FRAs, respectively, for each type of flood hazard listed in Section 2.2. This Appendix provides supplementary technical information to the guidance given in Chapters 5 and 6. Information on the selection and design of mitigation measures for developments at risk of flooding is given in Appendix A3.

A Level 3 FRA should be carried out under the direction of a qualified and competent person (Appendix A4), and as such this guide provides only summary advice on the techniques which may be used, and the factors which may need to be considered.

A2.1.   LEVEL 1 FLOOD RISK ASSESSMENT

The purpose of Level 1 flood risk assessment is to identify (Table 5.3):

- the flooding hazards which may pose a risk to the proposed development, or which the development may affect so as to increase flood risk elsewhere

- whether the proposed development may obstruct maintenance access to watercourses or flood defences or affect the integrity of a flood defence

- whether the development may lead to an increase in runoff.

The following sections provide guidance on the sources of information that may be used to assess whether the nature of the proposed development is such that a Level 2 FRA is required. A Level 1 FRA must consider all potential flooding hazards. **The decision not to proceed with a Level 2 FRA should be taken only when a Level 1 FRA clearly demonstrates that a development is not at risk of flooding and will not result in an increase in flood risk elsewhere.**

A2.1.1   Level 1 FRA of potential flood hazards

The initial task in any FRA is to assess whether the development site is located within an area which is at risk of flooding. For the purposes of a Level 1 FRA it is necessary to consider whether the site lies within a "high" or "low to medium" risk zone, ignoring the presence of any existing flood defences, as defined by the national planning policy guidance (Appendix A1).

This may be achieved by reviewing publicly available information, and undertaking a preliminary assessment of site characteristics. There is a wide range of sources that may provide information on flood risk and much may be available from the LPA/FDA. However, information is not available for every site, and any information available may not cover all of the potential flood hazards. Generally, more information will be available for fluvial and tidal flooding, while documented evidence of overland flow flooding, for example, is often scarce. Possible sources of information are discussed below.

Table A2.1 lists a number of key factors that should be considered during a Level 1 FRA, which are discussed in more detail below. These factors should be considered for all relevant potential flooding hazards, along with any other information that may aid in the identification of an area that is at risk of flooding. This table can be used to summarise the findings of a Level 1 FRA study. If the answer to a question is "YES" then a tick should be placed in the box for any flood hazard which may be applicable for the site in question. The boxes shaded grey indicate the sources of flooding which are unlikely to be identified for each question. If sufficient information is not available to identify the specific source of flooding, then all possible sources should be ticked. If a tick is placed below any flood hazard then a Level 2 FRA will be required to assess flood risk issues relating to that hazard in more detail.

Table A2.1 *Level 1 FRA Summary*

Question	Fluvial	Sea	Estuaries	Groundwater	Overland flow	Artificial drainage systems	Infrastructure failure
Is the development site next to the sea or any watercourse shown on Ordnance Survey maps?				▨		▨	▨
Is the development site, or part of the development site, identified as being at risk of flooding within available documentation?							
If a strategic flood risk assessment is available, is the development site, or part of the development site, identified as being at risk of flooding?							
If a flood zone map is available, is the development site, or part of the development site, within a High Risk zone[1]?				▨	▨	▨	▨
If a flood zone map is available, is the development site, or part of the development site, within a Low to Medium Risk zone[1]?				▨	▨	▨	▨
If a flood zone map is not available, is the development site, or part of the development site, situated on alluvium based on consideration of geological maps of the area?							
If there is an existing property on, or next to the site at the same level, is the property within a flood warning area?							
Are the LPA/FDA aware of any existing, historical or potential flooding problems that may affect the site?							
Do the physical characteristics of the site suggest that it may be prone to flooding?							
If a flood zone map is not available, is the development site, or part of the development site below 10 mAOD AND does the FDA consider the development to be at risk of tidal flooding?	▨			▨	▨	▨	▨
Is the development located within a natural or artificial hollow, or at the base of a valley or at the bottom of a hillslope?							
Does examination of historical maps indicate any likelihood of flood risk at the site?							
Do the names of surrounding roads, areas or houses suggest the possibility of seasonal or historical flooding?							▨
Is the site likely to involve excavation / construction below existing ground levels (excluding foundations)?	▨	▨	▨		▨		▨
Is the land use upslope of the site such that the generation of overland flow may be encouraged, and can water from this area flow onto the site?	▨	▨	▨	▨			▨
Are there any artificial drainage systems on or next to the site, at the same level, or upslope of, the site?							
Is the development site protected by an existing flood defence?							
Is the development site protected by a flood control structure (eg flap valve, sluice gate, tidal barrier etc)?							
Is the development site located upstream of a culvert which may be prone to blockage?							
Are water levels in a watercourse located in or next to a development site controlled by a pumping station?							
Is the development site next to or downstream/downslope[2] of a canal?	▨	▨	▨				
Is the development site downstream/downslope[2] of a reservoir or other significant water body?	▨	▨	▨				

1   Refer to national planning policy guidance for the definition of zones (Appendix A1).

2   If a development site is downslope of such features, flooding may occur in the event of failure of a water retaining structure. Those developments downstream of a reservoir, canal or other feature will be at risk only if they are sufficiently close to the source to be at risk of inundation following failure of the infrastructure in question.

Sources of information for Level 1 FRAs

Indicative flood plain maps/flood zone maps

Indicative flood plain maps are available for fluvial and tidal flooding for England and Wales on the Environment Agency website <www.environment-agency.gov.uk>. These were produced as part of a national flood hazard mapping exercise and are indicative of the general area that could be affected by flood events, overtopping or breaching of flood defence structures. The mapped flood plains nominally relate to the 1 per cent fluvial flood plain and the 0.5 per cent tidal flood plain, although in some areas the maximum-recorded flood extent may be shown. Equivalent indicative flood plain maps for Scotland are held by SEPA. National Assembly for Wales (2003a) includes interim maps of flood risk zones for Wales. These were produced based on a variety of information sources, including British Geological Survey drift geology maps.

The indicative flood plain maps are a valuable source of readily available information and can allow a rapid assessment of the likelihood of flooding from watercourses for a given site. However, it should be realised that the accuracy of the maps is limited due to the difficulty of accurately mapping flood hazard across such a large area, and therefore the results should be treated with caution.

Indicative flood plain maps are currently based on data from a variety of sources, which are of variable quality and detail (National Audit Office, 2001). They are based on a variety of modelling studies and historic flood levels. The maps do not differentiate between those areas that are currently undefended, and those areas that are protected against floods up to the effective level of an existing flood defence. They do not currently include the effect of climate change or the effect that local structures (eg bridges) will have on local flood levels.

Work is currently ongoing to develop the indicative flood plain maps and they are likely to be updated at regular intervals (Environment Agency, 2003c). This includes the production of a 0.1 per cent extreme event flood plain map and more detailed mapping of flood zones and flood hazard (flood depth etc). It is therefore recommended that, whenever a publicly available flood plain map is used to assess flood risk at a site, any available associated information on how the mapping was carried out be obtained from the FDA and reviewed.

If no other information is available then, for the purposes of a Level 1 FRA, the extent of the 0.1 per cent extreme event flood plain may be estimated from the areas mapped as overlying alluvium on a British Geological Survey drift geology map. Such a mapped flood plain is likely to be approximate due to the impact of changing climate, land use and watercourse channel geometry over time, but may provide an initial indication.

Strategic flood risk assessments

In addition to development control responsibilities, LPAs are responsible for the production of strategic planning documents to control the development process. In order to assist in the development of such strategies LPAs may undertake strategic flood risk assessments (SFRAs). These are studies which allow more detailed examination of the likely appropriateness of developing sites within a planning area, within the context of national planning policy and local needs. The results of SFRAs allow LPAs to refine their local plans on a more detailed basis than is possible using indicative flood plain maps. The results of SFRAs can be very useful in determining the flood risk to a proposed development site. They may provide information on flooding issues, such as detailed estimated flood levels, depths and velocities and possibly acceptable development types and applicability of mitigation measures.

Existing documentation relating to flooding problems and flood risk management

The most valuable information regarding potential flood risk to a site is information on previous flood events that have occurred within the area. Consultation with the FDA may allow current or potential flood risk issues to be identified. The FDA may hold information on the extent of areas affected by previous floods. The FDA should also be able to advise whether the location of a proposed development lies within an area for which a flood warning scheme is operated.

In addition to direct consultation with the FDA, there are a number of further sources that may provide information on flood risk and which may be readily available for the area in which a development site is located. Local libraries are often an excellent source of information on historical floods that have affected a particular area. Local newspapers, local history books and local interest groups may also provide useful information, and some of these may be found on the Internet. The amount of information available will vary throughout the UK, but some of the following documents may be available and may include information on flood risk (Table A2.2). **It is recommended that the LPA/FDA are consulted to ensure that the most up to date information sources are reviewed.**

Table A2.2 *Potential sources of information on flood risk*

Information source	Contents	Responsible agency
Strategic flood risk assessments	Flood risk mapping and management strategies	LPA
Structure plans[1]	Strategic approach to flood risk control	LPA
Local plans[1]	Identification of areas at risk of flooding and more detailed approaches to flood risk control	LPA
Flood risk policy statement	Statement on flood risk management policies for an area	LPA / FDA
Annual/biennial reports	Identification of recent flooding problems/issues	Local authority
Sewage plans/sewer flooding reports/drainage area studies	Identification of location of sewerage and potential problems	Sewerage undertaker
Catchment flood management plans	Strategy for sustainable flood defence for river catchment areas, including identification of flooding problems	FDA
Local Environment Agency plans	Presentation of issues on a wide range of topics for river catchment areas, including flooding problems	FDA
Community strategies	Sustainable development aspirations	LPA
Water level management plans	Identification of water level management requirements of protected wetland areas	FDA
Shoreline management plans	Policy documents for sustainable coastal defence for coastal cells	FDA
Harbour management plans	Sustainable use of harbours	
Sea defence scheme design reports	Design of sea defence schemes, including modelling to assess design levels	FDA
Coastal habitat management plans (CHAMP)	Sustainable sea defence strategies for areas which may affect internationally important wildlife sites.	FDA / National Nature Conservation Agency[2]
Estuary management plans	Sustainable use of estuaries	National Nature Conservation Agency[2]
Heritage Coast management plans	Management options for Heritage Coast areas	LPA
Flood alleviation scheme design reports or project appraisal reports	Design report for flood alleviation schemes, including modelling to set design levels	FDA
Biodiversity action plans	Identify status and targets for habitats and species	National Nature Conservation Agency[2]

1 Following the proposed changes to the planning system in England, structure plans and local plans will be replaced by regional spatial strategies and local development frameworks (Section 4.4).
2 English Nature/Scottish Natural Heritage/Countryside Council for Wales/Northern Ireland Environment and Heritage Service.

DTLR (2001) and National Assembly for Wales (2003a) contain more information on the background to many of these documents.

A review of historical maps may also provide evidence that the site has experienced flooding problems in the past, and may therefore experience flooding problems in the future. Historical maps may indicate areas of bog or marsh, may show the presence of springs which may not be shown on existing maps, and may even include notes on them such as "liable to flood".

Site characteristics

A brief visual inspection of a proposed development site may enable a rapid assessment to be made of the potential for the site to flood. The topography, geomorphology, vegetation cover and land use at a site may reflect its tendency to flood. The susceptibility of a site to flooding may be suggested by the following characteristics:

- areas next to watercourses at a similar level to the bank top of the watercourse, especially where the opposite bank is at a higher level, or the development site is relatively flat

- areas of flat ground at a lower level than existing developments which surround them

- public parks and sports fields, particularly old established areas known as meadows

- areas upstream of a restriction to flow, either natural (eg rock outcrop, bend) or man-made (eg weir, bridge, culvert) in a watercourse

- areas next to and at a similar, or lower, level to existing developments with raised floor levels, raised ground levels or flood defences

- developments which will require the realignment or diversion of a watercourse

- areas of bog or marsh.

In coastal and estuarine areas the level at which the development site is located is likely to be the major indicator of flood risk. For the purposes of a Level 1 FRA, if a site is located above the level of the 10 mAOD Ordnance Survey contour it may be regarded as being free from risk of flooding from the sea. If a site is below this level, the FDA should be contacted and likelihood of the site being at risk of flooding from the sea should be discussed in more detail. Development sites located within the flood plain of the sea _and_ of a watercourse should be treated as at risk of estuarial flooding.

If an artificial drainage system is located within or next to a proposed development site it should be assumed, for the purposes of a Level 1 FRA, that this may pose a potential source of flooding. Artificial drainage systems are not typically designed to accommodate large flood events (Section 2.2.6) and are therefore likely to pose a flood hazard to a proposed development.

If the development site is reliant upon infrastructure to manage flood risk, is downslope/downstream of a canal or reservoir or could be affected by blockage of a pipe, culvert or bridge, then a Level 2 FRA will be required to assess flood risk due to infrastructure failure (Appendix A2.2.8).

Groundwater flooding typically occurs at sites located in relatively low-lying areas located on aquifers, such as Chalk. The presence of springs and/or winterbourne streams near to a site are a good indicator that groundwater flooding may be an issue in the area. The presence of aquifers at or near to the ground surface can be identified through a review of British Geological Survey (BGS) maps. The flood risk posed by groundwater in such areas should be discussed with the FDA.

Developments which are located at the bottoms of hillslopes, in valley bottoms and in hollows, or which are cut into hillsides may be prone to flooding from groundwater and/or overland flow.

This may especially be the case in areas that are downslope of land uses that may encourage the generation and transmission of overland flow. These include, but are not limited to:

- agricultural land which has been ploughed for arable use, especially if ploughing has been undertaken in an up-down slope direction rather than along the contours

- urban development or transport infrastructure which has resulted in an increase in impermeable area without formal drainage

- presence of capped landfill or past industrial sites, areas of compacted or artificial ground and areas where excavation down to bedrock has occurred (eg quarries)

- areas of commercial forestry, as forestry practices may result in increased runoff rates and disruption of drainage systems.

Place names

Names of roads, buildings and areas can suggest that an area may be susceptible to flooding (eg "River Street", "Mill", "Marsh" etc).

A2.1.2   Level 1 FRA for sites close to watercourses and existing flood defences

It is important that developments do not interfere with the maintenance operations of the FDA, as to do so may lead to an increase in flood risk at the development site and elsewhere. In many locations the FDA will require access to a watercourse to carry out inspection and maintenance. It is also vital that a development does not compromise the integrity of any structures used for flood defence. For these reasons, FDAs may require consent for any work within a specified distance of certain watercourses and flood defences (Appendix A1). Structures which act to protect areas from flooding can be formal or informal (Box A2.1).

Box A2.1   *Formal and informal flood defence structures*

Formal flood defence are structures specifically designed to act as flood defence structures, and typically comprise walls or embankments (see Appendix A3.3.8).

Informal flood defence structures can include existing walls, buildings, embankments or areas of natural ground (eg sand dune systems) not specifically designed to perform a flood defence function. Informal defences cannot be relied upon to provide a flood defence as they may collapse or be bypassed during flood conditions.

Informal flood defence structures cannot be treated as flood defences when considering flood risk to a development. However, if a development does come within close proximity to an informal structure that provides protection to areas outside the development site, the potential flood defence function of these structures must not be compromised.

It is recommended that the FDA be consulted to ascertain whether a development is within close proximity to a flood defence. A development would be deemed to be within close proximity of a flood defence (whether formal or informal) if it is sufficiently close that it could potentially compromise the safe and efficient operation and maintenance of the flood defence, or could damage the integrity of the flood defence system. The FDA should be able to provide details on the location of formal flood defence structures around a development site, and of their requirements for maintenance access. They may also be able to provide additional information, such as design details, estimated standard of protection, and condition assessment, although this information will not be available in all cases. Informal flood defences should be identified during a site walkover.

In the absence of any other information, if the proposed development is within 15 m of a flood defence structure, or a structure which could potentially provide a flood defence function, then it should be assumed that the development may affect the flood defence and should be deemed to be within close proximity for a Level 1 assessment.

If the development is within close proximity of a watercourse or flood defence structure, or may result in the severance of maintenance access, a Level 2 assessment of the potential impact of the development on the FDA's access requirements and the integrity of the flood defence should be undertaken.

A2.1.3   Level 1 FRA for management of development runoff

In general, any development that will potentially increase runoff volumes and rates will need to have an associated FRA carried out to assess the feasibility of managing runoff, and the applicability of Sustainable Drainage Systems (SUDS). This is likely to include any development in which the permeability of any area of land is decreased and/or where the drainage of the land is improved.

Consideration of the likely impacts of the proposed development on runoff should take into account not only the current development proposals, but also any future growth in impermeable area which may be expected to occur over the lifetime of the development.

Development sites that are located on previously developed land (brownfield sites) and which will not increase impermeable areas or alter drainage systems may not require further consideration of runoff impacts. However, redevelopment of brownfield sites provides opportunities for betterment, as it may be possible to reduce runoff rates and volumes compared to the existing situation. The ideal situation is for runoff rates and volumes following the development to be returned to greenfield conditions, and in some instances the LPA/FDA may request that this is done. Level 2 FRA of development runoff management is therefore often advantageous for brownfield redevelopment.

If the development is to be drained to a public sewer, the sewerage undertaker will often perform the role of the FDA, and will usually have attenuation requirements based on the capacity of the existing sewer to carry storm flows. The local FDA will normally also be involved in consideration of runoff as the sewer system will usually outfall into a receiving watercourse. Justification will be required if it is proposed to drain the development directly to a watercourse.

If the development drains directly to the sea, or a watercourse which is not sensitive to changes in runoff rates and volumes, a Level 2 FRA is unlikely to be necessary. If the development is considered to be "small" by the LPA/FDA, such that any changes to existing runoff rates caused by the development would be expected to be negligible, consideration of development runoff management within a FRA may not be necessary. If it is believed that a proposed development fits any of these criteria, this should be agreed with the LPA/FDA.

A definitive statement of what makes a development "small" in terms of development runoff is not possible within this guide as this will vary across planning areas and, as such, if a development is considered to be "small", this should be discussed with the LPA/FDA.

In some cases the system that is to receive runoff from a development site may be especially sensitive to potential changes in runoff rates and volumes. In these cases the FDA may request that modelling of these systems is undertaken in association with examination of development runoff management, to assess the impact of the development on flood risk. Systems that may be particularly sensitive to changes in runoff from development sites include:

- canals
- watercourses for which the development site comprises more than 5 per cent of its total catchment area
- watercourses where the FDA is concerned that alterations to the timing of runoff from the development site may lead to coincidence with catchment peak flows
- watercourses which currently cause flooding problems to existing properties
- watercourses which are subject to tidelocking (eg tidally affected watercourses, pumped watercourses etc)
- watercourses in which small changes to flow may lead to large changes in water levels (eg which are currently subject to a significant restriction such as an undersized culvert).

A2.2. LEVEL 2 FLOOD RISK ASSESSMENT

A2.2.1 Level 2 FRA for fluvial flooding

The following should be read in conjunction with Chapters 5 and 6, and with reference to Appendix A2.1 and A2.3.1.

Identification of flooding mechanisms

The source(s) of flooding should have been identified during a Level 1 FRA. The first stage of a Level 2 FRA is to develop an understanding of the mechanisms of flooding at the site (Box A2.2). It is critical that it is determined whether flooding from the site is likely to be due to flooding from a single hazard, or whether it may be a result of conditions in two or more hazards. If two or more sources are involved then it is likely that the combined probability of flooding from the two sources will need to be considered (Section 2.1.3). If such a situation is found then procedures similar to those in Appendix A2.2.3 should be followed.

CIRIA C624

Box A2.2 *Case history – Level 2 flood risk assessment*

To provide additional housing stock, a local authority proposed to replace old industrial premises with new residential properties. As the site was in an area known to flood, a flood risk assessment was carried out. An extensive flood level and flow record was available for the area around the site, with a water level recorder being located on the opposite bank of the river from the site.

Using flow and level data provided by the Environment Agency, a rating curve was developed for the site. The 1 per cent flood level was estimated for the site and was found to be close to the maximum recorded level. Visual inspections and eyewitness evidence suggested that flood velocities across the site were negligible, and as the proposed development would replace existing buildings, it was concluded that the proposed development would not increase flood risk upstream or downstream of the site.

Based on the existing information, a masterplan for the site was developed which took into account the flood risk issues at the site.

During the site walkover visit it may be possible to identify areas of the site which will convey flood flows and areas where flood waters will be very slow moving or static (washlands). Flood paths and key hydraulic constraints may also be identified, and it should be possible to assess the required location and frequency of model cross-sections which would need to be used if hydraulic modelling was required for a Level 3 FRA.

If the site is located next to or upstream of a significant constriction, such as a bridge or culvert whose cross-sectional area is small relative to that of the channel/flood plain, or which has a low soffit level, it may be necessary to consider the potential impact on flood levels of blockage of the opening by debris. Appendix A2.2.8 provides some guidance on the methodology to be followed when considering this issue.

Identification and review of flood level data

A Level 2 FRA for fluvial flooding should include a search for any information about past flood levels at the site. The FDA should be consulted to see whether it holds, or is aware of, any data regarding observed flood levels at or close to the site. If the site is close to a canal then the canal operator may also hold flood level information.

Useful data includes:

- recorded water levels from water level recorders or gauging stations
- observed flood levels surveyed following a flood event
- flood maps produced following flood events
- aerial photographs, photographs or videos of flood events
- flood marks on nearby buildings or other structures
- accounts of inundation extents or flood levels during large flood events.

While rare, videos of past flood events are especially useful as they can provide direct evidence of flooding mechanisms and flood velocities at the site.

The availability, location, length of record, frequency of monitoring and accuracy of the data should be noted and, if possible, the data should be obtained and reviewed. If a level record is available at the site itself then the maximum recorded water level can be a useful parameter to obtain during the scoping study, although it should be noted that the maximum recorded water level may be less than the design flood level for the required standard of protection. The FDA may be able to indicate the approximate probability associated with recorded flood levels. If the available flood level data relates only to minor flood events then it will not be useful for direct estimation of the design flood level, but can be of use in calibration of a hydraulic model during a Level 3 FRA (Appendix A2.3.1).

Whilst existing flood level information can be very useful in assessing possible flood conditions at a development site, it provides information only about flood conditions under existing climatic conditions. When undertaking an FRA potential climate change effects should be taken into account.

If recorded flood level data are not available and models exist for the site, they may be used to obtain a better understanding of likely flood levels on the site. The LPA/FDA may be able to provide information about the results of hydraulic modelling studies, such as flood mapping studies, Strategic flood risk assessments, flood alleviation scheme feasibility studies or previous FRAs carried out close to the site. If possible, the full modelling reports and the model itself should be obtained and reviewed for adequacy. Even if the existing models are not able to accurately model conditions at the development site, their results may be used to define boundary conditions for any model used in a Level 3 FRA (Appendix A2.3.1).

The FDA may levy a charge for the provision of the information described above.

Historical accounts may be used to improve the understanding of likely flood conditions on the site. The British Hydrological Society (BHS) Chronology of British Hydrological Events (http://www.dundee.ac.uk/geography/cbhe) includes information on significant hydrological events (droughts, floods and extreme rainfall) for British rivers before 1930 and may provide some historical information on a site or river system. Because of the voluntary nature of this database, and the difficulty in finding historical records, this data source is not comprehensive, but is a good starting point when investigating historical flood information.

It may be useful to undertake a local newspaper and library search in an attempt to find information on previous flood events in the area. Local residents, community groups, local historical societies and parish councils may also be able to provide information. Bayliss and Reed (2001) provide more detailed guidance on the use of historical flood information. Anyone undertaking a review of historical accounts is encouraged to add their findings to the BHS Chronology described above.

Identification and review of available flood flow data

In addition to flood level data, information on flood flows is also very useful for fluvial flood risk assessments. Flood flow data is useful as it aids calibration of hydrological and hydraulic models and allows greater confidence to be achieved in the estimation of annual probability of recorded and predicted flood levels.

The FEH CD-Rom (Institute of Hydrology, 1999) includes locations of gauging stations used in development of the FEH (Appendix A2.3.1), and provides a rapid method of assessing the availability of gauging stations close to the site of interest. The National River Flow Archive (http://www.nwl.ac.uk/ih/nrfa/index.htm) is another useful source of information on gauging stations throughout the United Kingdom, and can be used to identify the location of any gauging stations near to the location of interest. Once these sources have been checked the FDA should be contacted to check the availability of gauging station data.

When checking the availability of flow data it is important that both the quantity and the quality of the flow data are checked. Some gauging stations have poorly defined rating curves for high flows, and the gauging station's history and reliability should be checked with the FDA. A preliminary assessment can be made for some gauging stations from the information provided on the National River Flow Archive website.

River flow data may be obtained from the FDA, who may levy a charge for the provision of this data. It is anticipated that flow data may become available for users on the Internet in the near future, although this facility was not available at the time of publication.

Identification of potential impacts to be considered

As noted in Chapter 3, developments within flood plains have the potential to have a variety of effects on fluvial flood risk. These may be summarised as:

- risk of flooding to the development

- increase in flood risk upstream

- increase in flood risk downstream due to loss of flood plain storage.

The actual impacts that will need to be considered will depend upon the flooding characteristics of the development site, and not all of these impacts will need to be considered at every development site. The flowchart in Figure A2.1 can be used to identify the impacts that need to be considered within a FRA for developments subject to fluvial flood risk.

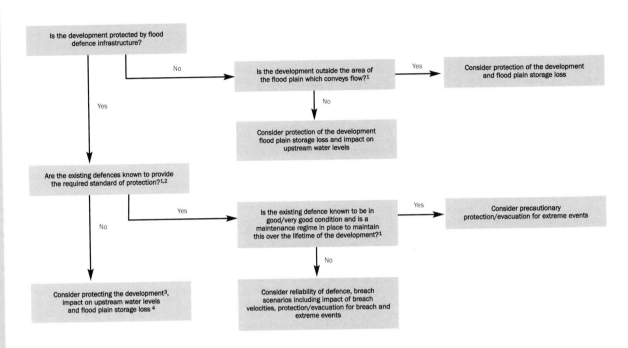

Figure A2.1 *Impacts to be considered in a fluvial FRA*

1   If existing information is inadequate the precautionary approach should be adopted and a "No" answer should be assumed.
2   Taking into account climate change over the lifetime of the development.
3   Development in such areas should only be considered if it does not conflict with the overall flood management strategy of the FDA.
4   Compensatory flood plain storage may not be required for proposed developments within brownfield areas, if the proposals bring benefits to other existing infrastructure through increased protection from flooding. Compensatory flood plain storage requirements should be confirmed with the LPA/FDA.

If the development is located behind a flood defence the recommendations for Level 2 FRA given in Appendix A2.2.8 should also be followed.

If visual inspection suggests that a development is likely to cause negligible loss of flood plain storage and/or insignificant increases in upstream water levels on a watercourse that is not sensitive to such changes, and where the potential for cumulative impacts is expected to be limited, then it may be appropriate to ask the LPA/FDA whether the requirement for quantitative assessment of such effects may be waived. In such cases it should still be demonstrated that appropriate measures have been taken to minimise any potential impact.

Preliminary assessment of acceptability of the development

If the work described above confirms that the proposed development is within a flood risk area then consideration should be given to identifying an alternative development site. If this is not practicable, and the possibility of development is to be pursued, a preliminary qualitative assessment of the feasibility of applying potential mitigation measures (Appendix A3.) may be undertaken. Such an assessment would involve identifying the type of mitigation strategy likely to be appropriate, given the nature of the flooding problem and the physical constraints present at the site.

Scoping of further work requirements

If the Level 2 FRA for fluvial flooding concludes that the development may be acceptable, the work required to undertake a full detailed (Level 3) FRA can be assessed. The work required will depend on the nature of the proposed development, the issues which need to be addressed and the nature of existing information on flood risk at the site.

Further guidance on the techniques to be used in a Level 3 fluvial FRA is given in Appendix A2.3.1. It is recommended that the method of analysis proposed for a quantitative assessment be agreed with the FDA before undertaking the Level 3 FRA.

A2.2.2   Level 2 FRA for flooding from the sea

The following should be read in conjunction with Chapters 5 and 6, and with reference to Appendix A2.1 and A2.3.2.

Identification of flooding mechanisms

The first stage of a Level 2 FRA is to develop an understanding of the mechanisms of flooding at the site. The key factor to ascertain during the Level 2 study is whether the site is prone to direct flooding from the sea, or whether the site is located behind a formal or informal flood defence (Appendix A2.1.2). If the development is located behind a flood defence the recommendations for Level 2 FRA given in Appendix A2.2.8 should also be followed. If the site is located behind a flood defence and is also at risk of flooding from a watercourse the recommendations given in Appendix A2.2.3 should also be followed.

Identification and review of flood level data

A Level 2 FRA for flooding from the sea should include a search for any information that could provide an estimate of flood levels at the site. The FDA should be consulted to see whether they hold, or are aware of, any data regarding observed flood levels at or close to the site. Useful data includes:

- predicted tidal characteristics
- recorded water levels from tide gauges
- observed flood levels surveyed following a flood event
- flood maps produced following flood events
- aerial photographs, photographs or videos of flood events
- flood marks on nearby buildings or other structures
- accounts of inundation extents or flood levels during large flood events.

The LPA/FDA may be able to provide information about the results of modelling studies, such as strategic flood risk assessments, Sea Defence feasibility studies or previous FRAs carried out close to the site, and may be able to indicate the approximate probability associated with recorded flood levels.

The FDA should, in most cases, be able to advise on indicative design water levels for an area, which may be used for preliminary assessment of development proposals, without the need for additional calculations. These water levels are likely to include an element of tidal surge, so levels published in tide tables should not be used without consideration of the potential effects of surges and waves.

The degree of exposure of a coastal area will affect the potential for wave generation and can be an important factor to consider. Detailed assessments of coastal flooding problems frequently involve joint probability analyses of still water level and wave combinations. This is a highly complex undertaking for which specialist advice should be sought.

Preliminary assessment of acceptability of development

For a Level 2 study it is recommended that the level method (Appendix A2.3.4) is used to extrapolate the design tidal level onto the development site to obtain a preliminary estimate of likely flood level.

If an alternative location outside of the flood risk zone cannot be found, then Figure A2.2 provides guidance on whether development on the site may be acceptable and what additional work needs to be carried out to quantitatively assess flood risk during a Level 3 FRA. Qualitative assessment of these issues should be undertaken during a Level 2 FRA. Preliminary assessment of the feasibility of providing mitigation measures to address these issues should also be undertaken.

If a sufficiently accurate design flood level is not available from the FDA, or it is anticipated that the level method (Appendix A2.3.4) will significantly overestimate flood levels at the proposed development site, a more detailed examination of flood risk may be required during a Level 3 study (Appendix A2.3.4). The scope of any additional works to assess coastal flood conditions for a development, including climate change considerations, should be agreed with the FDA.

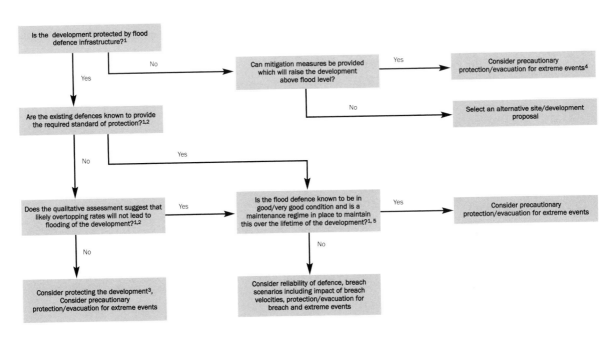

Figure A2.2 *Flowchart for developments at risk of flooding from the sea*

Notes

1   If existing information is inadequate the precautionary approach should be adopted and a "NO" answer should be assumed.
2   Taking into account climate change over the lifetime of the development.
3   Development in such areas should only be considered if it does not conflict with the overall flood management strategy of the FDA.
4   For many sea defence works associated with minor developments off-site impacts are unlikely to be required to be assessed. Developments in areas that are sensitive to change may cause significant impacts on coastal flood risk and erosion risk elsewhere and the assessment of geomorphological impacts may be required.
5   Taking into account the ability of the structure to withstand any expected overtopping.

A2.2.3   Level 2 FRA for estuaries and watercourses subject to tidelocking

The following should be read in conjunction with Chapters 5 and 6, and with reference to Appendix A2.1 and A2.3.3.

A Level 2 FRA for a watercourse subject to tidelocking will require the same work as that suggested for fluvial (Appendix A2.2.1) and coastal (Appendix A2.2.2) flood risk. In addition to this, the availability of data which can be used to estimate the combined effects of fluvial flows and tidal levels should be ascertained, as in such areas an assessment of the joint probability of fluvial flows and high sea levels is likely to be required. If records or descriptions of past flood events are available it is useful to identify whether the flooding was caused mainly by high watercourse flows, high sea levels or a combination of the two.

Developments at risk of tidally influenced flooding may be divided into two types:

- developments at risk of direct flooding from high water levels in an estuary

- developments at risk of flooding due to tidelocking of a watercourse protected from flooding from the sea by a flood defence and draining through a flow control device (eg flap valve, penstock, pumping station etc).

It is important that the type of flood mechanism is identified during a Level 2 FRA as the modelling needs associated with the different mechanisms vary (Appendix A2.3.3). Proposed modelling methodologies should be agreed with the FDA. For locations where it is agreed that fluvial flows will have a minimal impact on design flood levels, the FDA may accept that consideration of tidal conditions (Appendix A2.2.2) alone will be acceptable.

The risk of infrastructure failure (Appendix A2.2.8) should be considered for those developments located in areas protected by a flood defence.

Undertaking the above should allow a more accurate assessment of the flood risk to the site from the estuary or watercourse subject to tidelocking.

If an alternative location outside of the flood risk zone cannot be found, possible mitigation measures which could be employed should be considered (Appendix A3). If the Level 2 FRA concludes that a Level 3 FRA is required, the additional work needed can be scoped and agreed with the FDA.

It is unlikely that compensatory flood storage (Appendix A3.3.10) will be required for small developments within estuaries, as volumes within estuaries are dominated by tidal waters, although this may be required if the development could have a significant impact on the hydraulics of the estuary.

As storage in a watercourse subject to tidelocking is critical, compensatory flood storage (Appendix A3.3.10) will be required for developments in this situation. Consideration of the potential failure of the flood defence and flow control device (Appendix A2.2.8) should also be undertaken.

A2.2.4   Level 2 FRA for sites close to watercourses and existing flood defences

The following should be read in conjunction with Chapters 5 and 6, and with reference to Appendix A2.1.

The proposals for the development should be examined and the outline layout of the development should be designed to ensure that maintenance access is not obstructed, and that the development will not affect the integrity of any flood defence system. If the development may obstruct maintenance access, consultation should be undertaken with the FDA.

If the flood defence is to be relied upon to protect the property from flooding, then an assessment of the risk of infrastructure failure will be required (Appendix A2.2.8).

It is unlikely that a Level 3 FRA will be required to address this issue, although if the development includes realignment of a flood defence the FDA may require modelling to be undertaken to assess the impact of this on flood levels.

A2.2.5

Level 2 FRA for groundwater flooding

The following should be read in conjunction with Chapters 5 and 6, and with reference to Appendix A2.1.

A Level 2 FRA for groundwater flooding should be carried out under guidance from an expert hydrogeologist or geotechnical engineer and may be most effective if carried out in conjunction with a Level 2 FRA for overland flow flooding (Appendix A2.2.6). This could be undertaken as part of a geotechnical desk study for the site.

In addition to reviewing and confirming the analysis made in the Level 1 FRA, additional factors may be investigated to assess the potential risk from groundwater flooding. Groundwater flooding can be difficult to predict and close liaison with the LPA/FDA is essential.

A site walkover should be undertaken to assess on-site conditions and geological maps should be reviewed in detail to assess the hydrogeological characteristics of the site. The FDA and British Geological Survey (BGS) should be contacted to ascertain the availability of relevant data, and this should be collected and reviewed. Local water supply companies may also hold relevant data. Available data may include:

- records of flow from springs
- water levels in boreholes or wells
- recorded flood levels or flood marks
- groundwater flood maps
- aerial photographs or photographs of flood events.

Consultation with local residents may be an especially valuable method of finding information on past groundwater flooding events, as the lack of a designated organisation with responsibility for managing groundwater flooding means that official records of past groundwater flooding events may be sparse.

In addition to those factors listed in Appendix A2.1, indicators that the site may be prone to groundwater flooding include:

- if the development site is located near to the junction between geological strata of differing permeability
- if the development site is located near to a geological fault
- if the development site is located at a similar level to nearby springs, issues or stream headwaters

- if the development proposals include basements or excavations into the ground

- if the vegetation on site suggests periodic waterlogging due to high groundwater levels

- if nearby recorded borehole water levels reach levels close to the level of the site.

Undertaking the above should allow a more accurate assessment of the flood risk to the site from groundwater flooding.

If an alternative location outside of the flood risk zone cannot be found, possible mitigation measures which could be employed should be considered (Appendix A3).

If the Level 2 FRA concludes that a more detailed assessment of groundwater flooding is required then a Level 3 FRA should be undertaken. Detailed assessment of groundwater flood risk will depend upon the characteristics of the proposed development, the hydrogeological setting of the site and the availability of existing information, and may range from statistical analysis of recorded borehole water levels to large-scale hydrogeological modelling. Some studies may involve monitoring of groundwater levels. Guidance on detailed assessment of groundwater flood risk is beyond the scope of this guide, and expert hydrogeological advice should be obtained. The Geological Society of London <www.geolsoc.org> may be able to provide contact details for hydrogeological consultants.

A2.2.6   Level 2 FRA for overland flow flooding

The following should be read in conjunction with Chapters 5 and 6, and with reference to Appendix A2.1.

A Level 2 FRA for overland flow flooding should be carried out under guidance from an expert hydrologist or drainage engineer and may be most effective if carried out in conjunction with a Level 2 FRA for groundwater flooding (Appendix A2.2.5). In addition to reviewing and confirming the analysis made in Level 1, additional factors may be investigated to assess the potential risk of flooding due to overland flow. A site walkover should be undertaken to assess on-site conditions and local residents should be consulted. Soils and geological maps should be reviewed to assess the hydrological conditions. This should include a review of WRAP (Farquharson *et al*, 1978) and HOST (Boorman et al., 1995) maps. In addition to those factors listed in Table A2.1, indicators that the site may be prone to flooding due to overland flow include:

- if the site is located on, or downslope of, a soil type with a high runoff potential

- if evidence of soil erosion (rills, gullies etc) can be seen on the site

- if the vegetation on site suggests periodic waterlogging due to ponding of surface water.

The presence of a land drainage system on the site may indicate that the site was previously subject to overland flow flooding problems, as land drainage systems are typically installed to reduce water table levels within the soil. On such sites, the risk to the development and elsewhere due to exceedence or disruption of the land drainage system should be addressed (Appendix A2.2.7).

Undertaking the above should allow a more accurate assessment of the flood risk to the site from overland flow flooding.

If an alternative location outside of the flood risk zone cannot be found, possible mitigation measures which could be employed should be considered (Appendix A3).

If the Level 2 FRA concludes that a more detailed assessment of overland flow flooding is required then a Level 3 FRA should be undertaken. Detailed assessment of overland flow flood risk will depend upon the characteristics of the proposed development, the hydrological conditions of the site and the availability of existing information. Assessment of likely flow rates and volumes could be achieved using similar methodologies to those given in Appendix A2.3.1, whilst similar methods to those described in Appendices A2.3.4 and A2.3.1 could be used to assess likely flooding depths within flow pathways and areas where water may pond. However, these techniques may not be applicable in all situations and guidance on detailed assessment of flood risk due to overland flow is beyond the scope of this guide, and expert advice should be obtained.

A2.2.7   Level 2 FRA for flooding from artificial drainage systems

The following should be read in conjunction with Chapters 5 and 6, and with reference to Appendix A2.1.

A Level 2 FRA for flooding from artificial drainage systems should develop an understanding of the nature of the potential flood risk and allow the method of assessment of flood risk to be identified. It is important to identify who is responsible for operating and maintaining any artificial drainage system that may affect a site.

Flooding from existing sewerage systems is beyond the scope of the guide and should be investigated in consultation with the sewerage undertaker. CIRIA Report C506 (May *et al*, 1998) provides suggestions on mitigation measures which may be utilised to reduce sewer flooding problems.

The character and nature of any artificial drainage system within or next to the site should be examined during a site walkover. The catchment area of any artificial drainage system should be assessed, and the appropriate methodology for a Level 2 FRA identified:

- The flood risk from drains and ditches which have most of their catchment area within the development site should be assessed as part of the site drainage strategy (Appendix A2.2.9), although the additional runoff entering the site from outside the site boundary should be included in any calculations.

- The flood risk from drains and ditches which have most of their catchment area outside of the development site should be assessed following the methodologies described for fluvial flooding (Appendix A2.2.1).

A2.2.8   Level 2 FRA for flooding due to infrastructure failure

The following should be read in conjunction with Chapters 5 and 6, and with reference to Appendices A2.1 and A2.3.4.

Recommendations for Level 2 FRAs have been split into the three types of infrastructure as defined in Section 2.2.7, as the mechanisms of failure, data requirements and potential modelling methodologies vary between the different types of infrastructure.

The following sections discuss the work which should be undertaken to allow a more accurate assessment of whether the site is at risk of flooding due to infrastructure failure, and to assess the potential flood hazard caused by such an event. Once this has been undertaken, an initial assessment of the implications that this has on the viability of a proposed development can be made, and possible mitigation measures which could be employed can be identified.

Water infrastructure

Flood risk assessment in relation to reservoirs is beyond the scope of this guide, and it is recommended that consultation be undertaken with the reservoir operator and the FDA. CIRIA's *Risk management for UK reservoirs*, C542 (Hughes *et al*, 2000) provides details on how to assess flood risk associated with reservoirs.

If the site is next to a canal and the likely source of flooding is overtopping of the canal banks, then the canal should be treated as a special form of fluvial flood risk (Appendix A2.2.1). Consultation should be undertaken with the canal operator to develop an understanding of the inflows to, and flow control mechanisms present on, the canal system and an appreciation of the likely flood risk.

If the canal is located upslope of the development then the risk of the canal breaching should be assessed. The risk of seepage from the canal should also be discussed with the canal operator. A site walkover should be undertaken to assess the condition of the canal embankment to allow a preliminary assessment of the likelihood of breach and to collect any evidence of seepage from the canal. The canal operator should be consulted to assess the condition of the canal, the length of canal which would drain through any breach, the risk of flooding and potential solutions to the problem. The location of locks either side of the development site can provide a first estimate of the length of the canal that could drain through any breach, although any inflows into the canal system between these points should also be identified. If a quantitative assessment of flood risk due to canal failure is required then, depending on the situation, the methods described in CIRIA Report C542 (Hughes *et al*, 2000) or Appendix A2.3.4 may be applicable.

If the site is at risk of flooding due to the potential failure of a water main, liaison should be undertaken with the water supply company.

Flood defence infrastructure

When considering the potential effects of the failure of flood defence infrastructure (flood defences, flap valves, pumping stations etc) it is first necessary to develop an understanding of the existing condition of the flood defences and the potential failure mechanisms that exist. This will best be achieved through consultation with the FDA, and should include consideration of the following factors:

- the reasons for the presence of the defence
- type of the defence/form of construction
- design standard of the defence
- freeboard allowance
- defence age
- defence condition
- existing and likely future operation and maintenance regime
- pumping station capacity (if applicable)
- evidence of past failures, or failures of similar defences nearby
- any back-up systems available.

Assumptions should not be made about the design standard of protection for any existing flood defence infrastructure. This is because there may have been changes in design best practice, catchment characteristics and local hydraulic conditions since the flood defences were originally designed and constructed. The standard of protection provided by any flood defence infrastructure should be confirmed with the FDA.

Visual inspection of the defences should be undertaken during a Level 2 FRA as it will provide an indication of the existing condition of the defences. Realistic failure scenarios, including the method of failure, timing of failure relative to flooding and duration of failure should be assessed and agreed with the FDA.

It will be necessary to undertake an FRA for the source of flooding against which the flood defence is designed to protect (eg fluvial, coastal etc) in order to provide boundary conditions for the infrastructure failure analysis. For a Level 2 study it is recommended that the level method (Appendix A2.3.4) is used to obtain a preliminary estimate of likely flood levels which could occur in the event of infrastructure failure, and the feasibility of potential mitigation measures.

If it is thought that the level method is not sufficiently accurate, then the requirements of a more detailed Level 3 FRA (Appendix A2.3.4) should be scoped. It is important to define potential flood routes and areas at risk of flooding during a Level 2 study, from examination of topographic maps and a site walkover, as this information will aid interpretation of the system and may be required for modelling studies. This information will assist in deciding which type of modelling study, if any, will be required in a Level 3 FRA (Appendix A2.3.4).

If the proposed development is close enough to the flood defence that it may be subject to high velocities during a breach, then the potential impact of a flood defence breach should be qualitatively assessed during a Level 2 FRA, and the work required in a Level 3 FRA to address this issue should be scoped.

If failure of a flood defence is found to be a potential problem, the scope for raising, replacing or reinforcing the flood defence to reduce the risk of failure should also be assessed as part of a Level 2 FRA.

Bridge and culvert blockage

If the development site is located next to a watercourse upstream of a bridge or culvert which may be prone to blockage then a Level 2 FRA should be carried out to assess the need for more detailed consideration of the impacts of such blockage. Unprotected culverts may become blocked. However, debris and security screens on culverts also often become obscured with debris in floods and can significantly reduce the flow capacity (Box 3.3).

The risk associated with the potential blockage of the culvert should be assessed through a review of the characteristics of the culvert, screen, watercourse and catchment area. This should include consideration of:

- the nature of the culvert inlet, and the potential for blockage of any associated trash screen

- the nature of the watercourse upstream of the culvert, to assess the potential for debris to be carried downstream

- details of any existing operational arrangements for clearing culvert or screen blockages

- reports of any previous flood events due to blockage of the culvert or screen.

This will require liaison with the FDA and any other body which may be responsible for the maintenance of such a structure (eg highway authority).

Further details regarding the assessment of the risk of blockage to a culvert can be found in Environment Agency (2002).

If culvert blockage is found to be a potential problem the scope for modifying the culvert to reduce the risk of blockage should be assessed as part of a Level 2 FRA. The scope for designing the development to manage the potential consequences of any blockage of the culvert should also be considered during a Level 2 FRA.

If the risk of culvert blockage is found to be high, then a Level 3 FRA will be required (Appendix A2.3.4), but if it is found to be low then a Level 3 FRA of culvert blockage is unlikely to be required. The methods used in, and interpretation of the results of, this assessment should be agreed with the FDA.

A2.2.9   Level 2 FRA for management of development runoff

The following should be read in conjunction with Chapters 5 and 6, and with reference to Appendix A2.1.

A Level 2 FRA for management of development runoff should be used to identify existing conditions on site and opportunities and constraints relating to the development. A Level 2 FRA should include:

- identification of existing drainage systems on site

- confirmation of existing land uses on site

- identification of location of potential receiving watercourses/drainage systems

- confirmation of the requirements of the FDA/sewerage undertaker

- preliminary assessment of the feasibility of possible mitigation measures (Appendix A3.3.11)

- consideration of operation, maintenance and adoption issues

- identification of methodologies and additional work to be undertaken (if necessary).

The interaction of development runoff with potential flooding hazards for the site should be considered.

In addition to identifying the physical characteristics of the site which may influence existing site runoff and the appropriateness of mitigation measures (Appendix A3.3.11), consultation should be undertaken with the LPA/FDA/sewerage undertaker to develop an understanding of the likely constraints which will be placed on discharges from the site. **It is likely that the relevant bodies will require that the peak runoff rate from the development will not be any greater than that from the existing site, and that runoff volumes should also be controlled.** Wherever practicable, this should be achieved through the use of SUDS (Appendix A3.3.11).

When developing on a brownfield site it may be acceptable to ensure that the proposed development does not increase runoff rates and volumes above existing conditions. However, the redevelopment of a brownfield site should be seen as providing an opportunity for environmental enhancement and, as such, development drainage systems should aim to attenuate runoff to greenfield runoff rates.

The method by which greenfield runoff rate and development runoff is to be calculated should be agreed with the LPA/FDA before undertaking a Level 3 FRA. The methodologies for estimation of greenfield runoff rates and requirements for runoff attenuation from new developments are currently the subject on ongoing research and development. It is therefore recommended that the LPA/FDA are consulted to agree the methods to be used in FRA. Advice on the assessment and design of development runoff management measures can be found in Martin *et al*, (2000a; 2000b), HR Wallingford (2002; 2003a) and Scottish Executive (2001). As this issue is the subject of considerable ongoing research no further guidance is given on undertaking a Level 3 FRA for this issue and **it is recommended that the FDA be consulted to identify current design guidance.**

A2.3. LEVEL 3 FLOOD RISK ASSESSMENT

A2.3.1 Level 3 FRA for fluvial flooding

The following should be read in conjunction with Chapters 5 and 6, and with reference to Appendices A2.1 and A2.2.1.

The aim of the Level 3 FRA is to provide quantitative evidence that the proposed development can be designed such that it is not at an unacceptable risk of flooding, and that it will not increase flood risk elsewhere (Box A2.3), and typically includes the following steps:

- hydrological analysis to estimate flood flows

- hydraulic modelling to estimate existing flood conditions

- design of mitigation measures required to prevent flooding of site, and to avoid an increase in upstream water levels and loss of flood plain storage. Hydraulic modelling to demonstrate the effectiveness of these measures may be required.

Box A2.3   *Case history – complex Level 3 fluvial flood risk assessment*

A local planning authority required the developer of a proposed major development in the centre of a major city to provide a detailed flood risk assessment in support of a planning application.

Because of the scale of the proposed development and the complexity of the river system to be modelled – which included control structures – flow and level measurement stations were installed throughout the hydraulic system as part of the FRA, addressing the lack of available information in the study area. Flow and level data were collected to aid the calibration and validation of the hydraulic model.

Prediction of flood levels in this complex urban environment was achieved through the construction of a fully hydrodynamic two-dimensional hydraulic model linked to one dimensional elements, to better represent the interaction between overland flows, culverted and channel flows. This involved the collection of additional survey data at the site and throughout the urban area, collection of asset information from the water authority, and the construction of the two-dimensional hydraulic model. The model was used to produce comparisons of flood risk between the baseline situation, the development proposal and various mitigation options.

Predicted flood extents

Methods which may be used for hydrological analysis and hydraulic modelling are described below.

Hydrological analysis to estimate flood flows

The *Flood Estimation Handbook* (FEH), produced by the Institute of Hydrology (1999), is the current basis for estimation of flood flows within watercourses, and supersedes the *Flood Studies Report* (NERC, 1976). The FEH uses a Digital Terrain Model of the United Kingdom to automatically estimate key hydrological catchment descriptors for the catchment area draining to any point on a watercourse. These catchment descriptors can then be used to estimate flood flows. If appropriate watercourse flow data are available these estimates can then be refined to increase confidence in flow estimates.

FEH methods are suitable for estimating flood flows for watercourses with catchment areas greater than 0.5 km². For catchment areas smaller than this alternative methods should be used. Techniques which may be applicable in these situations include ADAS (1980) and Marshall and Bayliss (1994). Current guidance on the estimation of runoff from small areas is given in HR Wallingford (2003b).

It is important that the uncertainties inherent in these estimation techniques are acknowledged. In the absence of suitable local flow data, estimates using these methods are potentially quite inaccurate. For large developments the installation of a flow or level gauge should always be considered, since a relatively short record can provide useful data with which to refine estimates of key model parameters. When undertaking a FRA it is also important that the sensitivity of the development to potential climate change effects on flood flows is assessed.

Hydraulic modelling

Once design flood flows have been derived for a site, hydraulic modelling is likely to be required to estimate flood levels. It may be possible to estimate design flood levels without hydraulic modelling for sites which have a long record of recorded flood flows and levels by developing a rating curve for a site, but in most situations hydraulic modelling will be required. In order to produce estimates of flood levels, hydraulic models require the data listed in Table A2.3.

Table A2.3 *Data requirements for hydraulic modelling of flood levels*

Model requirement	Data source
Design flood flows	Hydrological analysis
Channel and flood plain cross-section survey, including structures and walls/embankments	Survey commissioned by those undertaking FRA, unless an existing survey is available from the FDA or elsewhere
Upstream and downstream boundary conditions	Can be observed water levels, predicted water levels from an existing model or water levels estimated on the basis of hydraulic principles
	Available boundary condition data should be identified in the Level 2 FRA
Roughness coefficients for channels and flood plains and hydraulic coefficients for hydraulic structures	Can be estimated by an experienced user during site walkover survey. Ideally, can be confirmed during calibration of hydraulic model to observed flood levels (identified during Level 2 FRA)

There are three types of hydraulic model which are typically used in fluvial FRA, and these are described in more detail below:

(i) Typical section method.

(ii) Steady-state backwater model.

(iii) Hydrodynamic model.

All of these models are one-dimensional as they only calculate flow in the downstream direction. Such calculations do not explicitly model the complex three-dimensional mechanisms which occur during a flood within a watercourse/flood plain system. However, in most situations they produce a reasonably accurate estimate of water levels. In addition to water levels these models can provide estimates of velocities.

In certain situations (eg around complex bridge structures or in areas of very complex channel/flood plain geometry) more advanced modelling, including the use of physical models, may be required.

Given that for the majority of FRAs one-dimensional models will be appropriate, these are described in more detail below in increasing order of complexity.

Whichever type of model is used, a number of approximations and assumptions will be made when defining the parameters listed in Table A2.3, which will affect the model results. For any modelling study, it is essential that sensitivity tests are carried out to assess the effect of variations in key parameters (eg roughness coefficients, flood flows etc) on predicted flood conditions.

Typical section method

This method (Highways Agency, 1995) uses a single channel/flood plain cross-section and an estimate of hydraulic gradient to predict water levels and velocities. This is a very simple model and as hydraulic gradient is difficult to predict accurately it should be used only where a recorded flood level at, or very close to, the design flood level is available to confirm the results of the modelling. It should be used only where the proposed development will impact on a very short reach of flood plain, and where the surrounding watercourse is straight and of relatively consistent geometry upstream and downstream of the site.

In most situations the typical section method will not be appropriate and the use of more advanced models will be required.

Steady-state models

These one-dimensional models simulate a single, time invariant water surface profile, based on the hydraulic characteristics of each cross-section. As most developments border relatively short lengths of watercourse, steady-state models will often be appropriate. However, these models take no account of storage or routing effects and cannot model the effect of water spilling into an area. Crowder (2003) reviews some of the capabilities and limitations of some of the currently available and widely used steady-state models.

Hydrodynamic models

Hydrodynamic models simulate the movement of flood waves through a watercourse/flood plain system and can predict the variation in level and flow at a point through time. Hydrodynamic models are more comprehensive than steady-state models as they take into account the storage effects within the watercourse/flood plain system and can often simulate the behaviour of devices whose operation can vary through time. However, as they are more complex they are more time-consuming and expensive to use. Crowder (2003) reviews the capabilities and limitations of some of the currently available and widely used hydrodynamic models.

A2.3.2 Level 3 FRA for flooding from the sea

The following should be read in conjunction with Chapters 5 and 6, and with reference to A2.1 and A2.2.2. During a Level 3 FRA (Box A2.4) it will usually be necessary to undertake the following analysis:

- estimate design flood levels at the coast, taking into account the influence of astronomical tides and surge effects

- estimate the impact of wave effects

- assess the adequacy of the proposed development design/mitigation measures.

Box A2.4   *Case history – Level 3 flood risk assessment for flooding from the sea*

A development was proposed in an area that is protected from flooding at high tide levels by an existing informal flood defence. These defences consist of raised sand dunes situated along the coast. A flood risk assessment was undertaken to assess the risk of flooding to the site should the flood defences be breached.

A design 0.5 per cent peak tide level was specified for the site by the Environment Agency, and a tide curve was determined based on the tide curve at nearby location given in published tide tables. This provided boundary condition data for the breach model, which was used to simulate the effect of a breach in the flood defences directly to the south of the site.

A two-dimensional flood routing program was used to calculate time travel across flood cells and simulate inundation extent, based on topographical data provided by the Environment Agency. Peak water depths and velocities across the site were determined from the model results and a flood plain outline was produced.

Extreme water levels of various annual probability of exceedence, including both tidal and surge effects, can be obtained by using Dixon and Tawn (1997), with the tidal curve being derived from Admiralty Tide Tables for the nearest port. Surge shapes can be estimated from recorded events. Design wave conditions for a location may be available in a relevant Shoreline Management Plan (Worth and Cox, 2000). The combined probability of the components of a tidal flood event (Section 2.1.3) should be considered. Simm *et al*, (1996) provides guidance on simplified techniques for estimating appropriate combinations of still water level and wave height for use in design and analysis.

Depending on the situation, it may be necessary to estimate the likely volume of water and consequential flood depth due to overtopping of sea defences by wave action. Further details on methods of calculating design flood levels for coastal locations can be found in Simm *et al* (1996), McConnell (1998) and Besley (1999). Methods of assessing flood levels following the breaching of a coastal defence are described in A2.3.4.

For highly sensitive developments at some distance from a tide gauge, where the expected impacts of flooding may be considerable, it may be necessary to carry out computational coastal modelling to predict expected flood levels, under existing and proposed conditions.

A2.3.3   Level 3 FRA for estuaries and watercourses subject to tidelocking

The following should be read in conjunction with Chapters 5 and 6, and with reference to A2.1 and A2.2.3.

Estuaries

If the development is prone to flooding due to the combined effect of tidal and fluvial conditions within an estuary then the following modelling procedure is likely to be required:

- estimation of extreme tide levels and tidal curve (A2.3.2)

- estimation of flood flow hydrographs (A2.3.1)

- estimation of joint probability for a variety of tide and flood conditions

- hydraulic modelling of tide and flood conditions to derive estuary design flood levels (A2.3.1)

- If necessary, hydraulic modelling to assess the impact of the development on flood levels (A2.3.1).

Normally, hydrodynamic modelling will be required to assess the propagation of flood and tidal waves through the estuary. In complex situations where the development is expected to have a potentially major effect on the estuary two-dimensional modelling may be required and if this is the case specialist advice should be sought.

In larger estuaries, wind-generated waves can play a significant role in influencing the flood risk, and appropriate coastal modelling techniques should be used (A2.3.2).

Watercourses subject to tidelocking

If the development is located next to a watercourse which is subject to tidelocking (Box A2.5), the following modelling procedure is likely to be required:

- estimation of extreme tide levels and tidal curve (see A2.3.2) or design flood level hydrograph in the watercourse causing the tidelocking (A2.3.1)

- estimation of flood flow hydrographs in the watercourse subject to tidelocking (see A2.3.1)

- estimation of combined probability for a variety of tide and flood conditions

- hydraulic modelling of tide and flood conditions to derive existing design flood levels along the watercourse subject to tidelocking, including simulation of control structures (A2.3.1)

- in association with a study into the management of development runoff (A2.2.9), hydraulic modelling to demonstrate the impact of the proposed development on flood levels

- if necessary, hydraulic modelling to assess the adequacy of proposed mitigation measures (A3).

Hydrodynamic modelling (A2.3.1) will be required as both peak flows and total flood volumes within a tidelocked watercourse are critical in determining flood levels.

Box A2.5 *Case history – development in an area at risk of tidal flooding next to a watercourse subject to tidelocking*

As part of the regeneration of a former power station site, residential development was proposed for an area next to a watercourse draining into an estuary via a flapped outfall under a flood defence. Concern was raised about the flood risk posed to this area due to previous flooding of the town upstream, caused by tidelocking of high fluvial flows and overtopping of the sea defences.

A flood risk assessment was therefore carried out for the site. This included assessment of the risk of overtopping of the existing sea defences and hydrodynamic modelling of the watercourse to assess flood levels due to the combined effects of high tidal levels and high fluvial flows. Modelling was carried out to assess existing and future water levels, and to assess the flood risk that would occur if the flap valves on the tidal outfall were to jam open.

The results of this model were used to guide the design of the development. A new, higher, sea defence was constructed behind the existing sea defences to improve the standard of protection to the development area and the town to the 0.5 per cent level (including an allowance for climate change). This included the managed realignment of a section of sea defence, to encourage the reinstatement of an area of saltmarsh. To provide additional protection to areas of proposed housing, much of the development area is being raised to above flood level.

A new tidal outfall is to be provided for the watercourse, which, together with the creation of a section of two-stage channel in the ditch, will offset the potential impact of the increase in runoff from the development. The modelling study also demonstrated the need for a penstock system to be incorporated on the new tidal outfall to provide back-up to the flap valves.

A2.3.4   Level 3 FRA for flooding due to infrastructure failure

The following should be read in conjunction with Chapters 5 and 6, and with reference to Appendices A2.1 and A2.2.8. The following discussion refers to methods of assessing the consequences of failure of flood defence infrastructure and culvert blockage (Box A2.6). The method of assessment of water infrastructure is dependent on the situation (Appendix A2.2.8).

Box A2.6 *Case history – flood risk assessment for infrastructure failure*

A proposed development involved the conversion into flats of an historical mill building. The mill building was located next to a main river, behind an existing flood bank.

As part of the development design, a flood risk assessment was undertaken to assess the standard of protection provided by the flood bank. Geotechnical and topographical assessment of the existing flood bank was undertaken to assess its ability to provide protection during a 1 per cent flood event. The Environment Agency provided predicted flood conditions for the rivers, based on an existing model, and these were used to assess the adequacy of the flood bank. This work found that the flood embankment had been breached in places, and that it would not be structurally adequate to withstand the design flood.

Recommendations were made to rebuild the flood bank to enhance protection and to utilise flood proof construction in the new development which would mitigate the potential effects of flooding should a breach occur.

On-site attenuation of runoff from the development was also recommended to reduce the potential effect of the development on downstream flood risk.

Before assessing the impact of the failure of infrastructure it is first necessary to carry out analysis to define the design flood conditions in the flooding source which the infrastructure is designed to manage. For example, before assessing the failure of a sea defence it is necessary to define the flood conditions in the sea (Appendix A2.3.2), and before the impact of culvert blockage is assessed, the flood conditions on the watercourse in the absence of blockage must be defined (Appendix A2.3.1). Only once this has been done can the impact of infrastructure failure be assessed.

As noted in A2.2.8, if infrastructure failure has been identified as a potential risk to a proposed development, the FRA should first consider whether it is practicable to modify the infrastructure to manage this risk. The FRA should also consider the scope for designing the development to manage the potential consequences of any infrastructure failure.

Flood defence infrastructure failure

Quantitative assessment of the potential impacts of failures of flood defences is not straightforward and requires expert judgement. This is because assessing the impact of a breach failure involves assessing the breach failure mechanism, breach base level, suggested scenarios for breach width, time of closure, and the timing of the breach relative to the flood event. Similarly, when assessing the potential failure of a flap valve, penstock or pumping station, realistic scenarios of failure mechanisms and durations should be applied.

As part of a Level 3 FRA for flooding due to flood defence infrastructure failure, it may be necessary to undertake investigations to develop an understanding of the likelihood and mechanisms of failure. This could include surveys to examine the composition and condition of a flood bank, the structural condition of a flood defence wall, a mechanical and electrical inspection of a pumping station and testing of a penstock. These investigations can then form the basis for any assumptions about failure conditions during a modelling study.

There are three possible methods of estimating flood volumes due to failure of flood defences, of increasing complexity (Hamer *et al*, 2000):

1 **Level method:** assume flooding of the area will occur up to the peak level of the design storm event in the body of water posing the flood risk. This takes no account of the effect of restrictions to inflow through the failed defence, the length of time which the failure may occur for or the length of time that flood levels will be high enough to cause inflow. This method is likely to overestimate flood levels in many situations, and does not provide an estimation of flood velocities.

2 **Volume method:** using this method the total volume of water flowing through the failed defence is calculated and distributed over the area behind the defence to calculate a flood level. This takes no account of the possible effect that restrictions to flows (eg culverts, weirs, embankments) and routing effects may have. This method can potentially lead to overestimation of flood levels in some areas and underestimation in others. This method provides only estimates of velocities through the breach and average velocities over wide areas.

3 **Dynamic method:** use of a hydrodynamic model to simulate the propagation of the flood wave caused by the failure of the defence along channels and over the land surface. This is the most accurate method and can provide distributed velocity information.

It is recommended that the level method is used in the first instance as it requires no assumptions to be made about the size and duration of infrastructure failure. Only if this appears to be unrealistic, and mitigation measures to protect against flooding are not practicable, or if flood velocities are likely to be of concern, will a more detailed method be required. The volume method should only be applied where no significant routing effects would be expected.

When designing mitigation measures to protect a proposed development against potential infrastructure failure, it should be ensured that the mitigation measures do not significantly increase flood risk to existing developments beyond the proposed development site.

Bridge and culvert blockage

If the effect of culvert blockage on flood levels at a development site needs to be assessed then a hydraulic model (A2.3.1) should be used to simulate hydraulic conditions during culvert blockage.

A3 Mitigation measures for flood risk management

A3.1 MITIGATION MEASURES FOR FLOOD RISK MANAGEMENT

This Section provides a brief introduction to the types of mitigation measures that are available to address flood risk issues at a development site. The main types are listed in Box A3.1. Further details on each mitigation measure are given in the section identified in Box A3.1

Box A3.1   Measures to mitigate flood risk to a development

Mitigation measure	Section
Site selection	Appendix A3.3.1
Development zoning	Appendix A3.3.2
Raising floor levels	Appendix A3.3.3
Land raising	Appendix A3.3.4
Flood warning	Appendix A3.3.5
Flood proofing	Appendix A3.3.6
Design of channel and hydraulic structures	Appendix A3.3.7
Flood defences	Appendix A3.3.8
Developer contributions to strategic flood risk management	Appendix A3.3.9
Compensatory flood storage	Appendix A3.3.10
Management of development runoff	Appendix A3.3.11
Pumping	Appendix A3.3.12

The range of mitigation measures listed in Box A3.1 can provide a variety of functions. Table A3.1 indicates those mitigation measures that may be applicable to meet the objectives for a development that is sustainable in flood risk terms (listed in Box 5.1).

Table A3.1 *Applicability of mitigation measures to meet key sustainability objectives for new developments*

Objective	Select appropriate development site	Development zoning	Raising floor levels	Land raising	Flood warning	Flood proofing	Design of channel and hydraulic structures	Flood defences	Developer contributions	Compensatory flood plain storage	Management of development runoff	Pumping
Reduce flood risk to development	■	■	●	■	●	●[2]	●	●	●	x	■	●
Manage surface water runoff	●	■[1]	x	x	x	x	x	x	●	x	■	●
Avoid increase in upstream flood risk	■	■	x	x	x	x	●	x	●	x[3]	x	●
Avoid increase in downstream flood risk	■	■	●	x	x	x	x	x	●	■	●	x

■ Often acceptable   ● Sometimes acceptable   x Not applicable

[1] Zoning can be used to provide flow paths for extreme events which exceed the capacity of the formal on-site drainage system.

[2] Flood proofing is usually only acceptable as a secondary measure eg if used in association with raised floor levels, or to provide protection against an extreme flood event.

[3] Land regrading as part of compensatory flood storage works may also in some situations improve conveyance within the system.

While a variety of mitigation measures may be available to address a problem, some mitigation measures are preferable to others. This is because the reliability, cost, operation and maintenance requirements and potential environmental impacts of different mitigation measures vary (Appendices A3.3.1 to A3.3.12). Wherever possible, it is recommended that the development be located such that flood risk issues associated with the development are minimised. If the whole development site cannot be located outside a flood risk zone, development zoning should be considered so that features which are sensitive to flood damage are located outside that zone. Only if these measures are not practicable should alternative mitigation measures be considered.

A combination of mitigation measures may be needed to deal with the flood risk issues associated with a proposed development. Design of the development, including mitigation measures, is often an iterative process, as the introduction of a mitigation measure to address one problem may impact on another.

It is recommended that the proposals for any development which is potentially at risk of flooding should be discussed with insurers, to obtain confirmation of the terms on which they would be willing to provide insurance, given the proposed mitigation measures.

A3.2   KEY DESIGN CONSIDERATIONS

Whichever mitigation measures are employed it is essential that certain key criteria should be met. Table A3.2 provides a checklist to determine whether the proposed development is likely to be acceptable to the local planning authority/flood defence agency (LPA/FDA).

Table A3.2   *Acceptability of mitigation measures*

Criterion	YES/NO[1]
Is the residual flood risk to the development acceptable?	
Are adequate access arrangements available?	
Is the impact of the development on upstream water levels acceptable?	
Does the development cause no net loss of flood storage at all flood levels?	
Is runoff from the development going to be adequately controlled?	
Are the potential environmental impacts of the proposed development and mitigation measures acceptable?	
Are the operation and maintenance requirements associated with the proposed mitigation measures acceptable, and is it clear who is responsible for maintenance and operation?	
Has it been ensured that the development will not obstruct FDA maintenance access?	
Is the development designed such that any risks to health, safety and welfare will be appropriately managed?	
Will arrangements be made to ensure that future owners/operators/occupiers of the site will be aware of any residual flood risks, mitigation measures, and operation and maintenance requirements?	
Are the development proposals such that they will not compromise any strategic flood risk management policies for the area?	
Are the relevant consents required from the FDA likely to be given?	

[1] The development is unlikely to be acceptable if the answer to any of these questions is "No"

The design of any development which may affect the natural processes within a catchment should be consistent with the requirements of any river basin management plan which has been prepared under the Water Framework Directive (European Union, 2000). The FDA should be able to advise of the requirements of any such plan.

It is important to remember that mitigation measures will be effective only up to the magnitude of the design flood event. When the design flood is exceeded then the mitigation measures will not operate in the intended manner. The potential impact of floods in excess of the design flood is an important factor to be considered when developing the design of mitigation measures.

A3.3   FLOOD RISK MITIGATION MEASURES

The following sections describe the principal characteristics of a range of flood risk mitigation measures, which may be appropriate for use in the design of new developments.

A3.3.1   Development site selection

The simplest way to manage the majority of flood risk problems is to select a development site outside the flood risk zone.

Some developments are more sensitive to flood risk than others, and national planning policy guidance identifies many of the development types which should be located outside "low to medium" and "high" flood risk zones (Appendix A1). Developments which have potential to be damaged during flood events, and those which could subsequently release pollutants into the water environment, should also be located outside these flood risk zones.

Relocation of the development will not necessarily, in itself, manage runoff from a site, although relocation to a brownfield site – or to a site that drains to a less sensitive watercourse – may reduce the potential impact of runoff from a development.

A3.3.2

Development zoning

Careful planning of development layouts may allow flood risk to be managed in a development without the need for the construction of physical mitigation measures. Such solutions are beneficial as they can be very cost effective and can minimise the impact that the development may have on flood risk. A properly zoned development has similar benefits to development constructed on raised land (Appendix A3.3.4), without the costs associated with land raising and other mitigation measures required to avoid an increase in upstream and downstream flood risk. Figure A3.1 illustrates the main methods by which development zoning can be used to reduce flood risk to a development

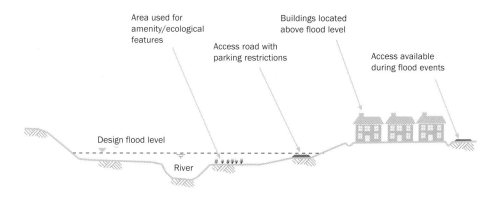

Figure A3.1 *Zoning techniques to reduce flood risk*

Green space

One method of reducing flood risk through development zoning is to plan open spaces such as parks, gardens, playing fields, allotments, nature conservation sites etc, within the flood risk zone, and accept that these areas will flood. Such land uses are generally less sensitive to flood damage than other forms of development and may therefore be acceptable within flood risk areas. Such design is also useful when considering flood routing requirements for extreme events when designing development runoff management systems (Appendix A3.3.11).

It should be recognised that flooding may cause damage to areas which are allowed to flood, through erosion, pollution and deposition of debris and sediments, and this may lead to the areas being unusable for longer periods than the duration of the flood event itself. Such areas should therefore be designed carefully.

If open spaces are to be proposed in areas of flood plain which convey flow, they must be kept free of significant obstructions to flow (eg fences, buildings) and materials which may be carried off by flood water to possibly cause a blockage or pollution incident downstream. The potential effect of any obstruction is likely to be exacerbated during a flood event as it may collect debris, which would cause an additional increase in upstream flood levels. For this reason it is unlikely that developments which propose to place private gardens within areas of flood plain which convey flow will be acceptable, as there is potential for the erection of fences, sheds etc following development. If allotments are planned, sheds should be located above design flood level.

Planting plans should be considered carefully for areas which are to be allowed to flood. Large vegetation can interfere with flood flowpaths, trap debris and cause blockages downstream if uprooted during a flood event. Smaller vegetation is preferable for these areas and tree planting should be restricted. The FDA may be able to provide guidance on appropriate plant species for such areas.

Areas which are designed to encourage public access should be appropriately signed so that users of the areas are aware of both the risk of flooding and the appropriate response. Such areas should be designed to flood progressively in a safe way, with no islands being formed and a suitable flood warning (Appendix A3.3.5) and evacuation procedure should be provided. Manholes should not be located in flood risk zones, unless designed with mechanisms to avoid covers lifting during a flood event, as open manholes may pose a safety hazard during and after a flood.

Car parks

In some circumstances, car parks may be planned for flood risk zones, as the car park infrastructure may not be sensitive to flood damage. The introduction of car parking into a flood risk area is not without risk because if vehicles are parked in the area when a flood occurs, considerable damage to the vehicles may occur. If the flood depth is greater than around 0.3 m then the vehicle may be carried off by the flood water (HR Wallingford, 2003a).

If such a feature is planned then it is essential that a flood warning and evacuation procedure is developed to allow vehicles to be removed from the area in advance of a flood event, unless expected flood depths and velocities are very low. As part of the evacuation procedure, alternative locations where cars may be parked during a flood event should be identified. Car parking in flood risk areas associated with residential developments is unlikely to be acceptable, due to the risk that residents may not be at home during the onset of a flood event.

Similar issues to those discussed for green spaces (see above) are related to the use of car parks in flood risk areas.

Access roads

Access roads may be suitable for location within flood risk areas, providing that there is an alternative access that will be operational during times of flood. Unless parking is restricted on such access roads, similar arrangements to those required for car parks will be required. Unless flood depths and velocities on the access road are very low, arrangements should be in place to ensure the closure of the access road when a flood is expected, including physical barriers to prevent vehicles from entering the flooded road. Guide posts should be provided either side of the road so that the location of the road can be identified during a flood event.

Industrial and commercial premises

In some cases, industrial and commercial premises may be located within flood risk zones. These may be acceptable if they can be designed to withstand the impact of flooding (Appendix A3.3.6). If such a development is proposed the impact of flooding on the economic viability of the business and the availability of insurance should be carefully considered.

Developments involving industrial processes which involve the use of potentially polluting substances (fuels, chemicals etc) should be designed in a way that these substances will not enter the water environment during a flood, preferably through designing the development such that these chemicals are stored and used outside the flood risk zone.

Similar consideration should be given to the location of areas that may be used to store goods and materials that may be carried off by flood water (eg timber). Proposed developments that include industrial and/or commercial premises in flood risk zones should be discussed with the FDA.

Acceptability of development zoning

There are a number of practical issues that may affect the appropriateness of the proposed development. Table A3.3 provides a checklist that, together with Table A3.2, should assist in deciding whether a proposed land use is likely to be appropriate for a situation.

Table A3.3 *Key considerations for development zoning*

Consideration	YES/NO[1]
Are the proposed land uses appropriate given the design flood level and velocity?	
Are the proposed land uses appropriate given the expected frequency of flooding?	
Are the proposed land uses appropriate given the expected duration of loss of amenity[2]?	
Are arrangements in place for undertaking clean-up operations following flooding?	
Are arrangements proposed which would inform people of the flood risk associated with an area?	
Will arrangements be made to ensure safe and timely evacuation of people and any features vulnerable to flood damage from the flood risk zone?	
Are there likely to be problems with erosion, sedimentation and/or water quality during and following flood events that may threaten the viability of the uses?	

[1]   The development is unlikely to be acceptable if the answer to any of these questions is "No".
[2]   Related to the frequency of flooding, the expected duration of flood event and the time required for clean-up operations.

A3.3.3

Raising floor levels

One method of reducing flood risk to a development is to raise the floor level of buildings to above flood defence level. Car parking and utility areas may be located at lower levels.

Ideally this will be achieved by appropriate zoning (Appendix A3.3.2) or land raising (Appendix A3.3.4). However, in some cases it may be feasible to design the development so that the ground floor is allowed to flood, provided that the use of the ground floor is such that flooding would be acceptable. Indeed, DTLR (2001) suggests that the use of upper levels of converted structures, such as warehouses, for housing – with appropriate uses at a lower level – may be acceptable. Such a design may also be appropriate for new build developments but, in both cases, a number of factors should be taken into account when deciding on the appropriateness of such a mitigation technique, as discussed below.

The principal benefit of this mitigation technique is the reduction of flood risk to property. To maintain this benefit, ground floors should be designed as open plan public spaces, such as car parks or utility areas. Provision of private garages or other enclosed private spaces should be avoided, both due to the risk of vehicular damage and because this may encourage the future storage of potential pollutants (eg pots of paint, oil etc) and white goods (eg washing machines, freezers etc) within flood risk zones. If car parks are proposed, reference should be made to Table A3.3 to ensure their acceptability.

Special consideration should be given to safety if access to floor levels that are below flood defence level is to be provided by lifts. Lifts should be prevented from operating on such floors during flood events. Adequate flood warning (Appendix A3.3.5) and evacuation procedures should be put in place.

Bungalows and other single-storey buildings should not be developed in areas at risk of flooding, even in areas behind flood defences. Flooding of such properties can pose a significant safety risk and can lead to severe damage during flood events because the lack of an upper floor level makes movement of people and contents to above flood level very difficult. Buildings with two or more storeys may reduce the size of the ground floor vulnerable to flooding, provide a place of refuge for any person trapped by flooding, and provide more opportunity for temporary storage of contents during flooding and flood recovery.

Basements should not be included within the design of developments within areas at risk of flooding, unless basement areas are dry proofed (Appendix A3.3.6) and access is only provided from above flood defence level. Even with such measures in place basements should be used only for storage or waterproof utilities, and entry into basements should be restricted during flood events because of the potentially serious consequences of the inundation of basements by flood water.

Developments designed to allow the ground floor to flood freely also provide mitigation for potential downstream flood risk effects. In these cases the loss of flood storage associated with the development will be limited to the volume taken up by the walls of the buildings. This may reduce the need for compensatory flood storage works (Appendix A3.3.10).

Where the raising of floor levels in a building is to be achieved by placing the building on stilts with an open lower floor, there is a significant risk that flooding of the ground floor may be restricted in the future, either due to accidental blockage by debris or filling in of the space by future owners of the development. Proposed developments within a flood risk zone that have raised floor levels are likely to be acceptable to the FDA/LPA only if it can be demonstrated that measures (such as legal agreements) are in place to prevent inappropriate use or alteration of the ground floor in future.

Table A3.4 provides a checklist that, together with Table A3.2, should assist in deciding on the appropriateness of a proposed building floor level.

Table A3.4 *Key considerations for building floor levels*

Consideration	YES/NO[1]
Does the building have more than one floor?	
Are suitable flood warning and evacuation procedures proposed (see Appendix A3.3.5)?	
Is the construction acceptable and appropriate for the use of the development, such that the structures, fittings and contents below flood level will not be damaged by flooding? (See Appendix A3.3.6)	
If the proposed building has a basement, is this feature essential and have appropriate measures been proposed to avoid damage and health and safety risks during a flood event?	
Are flood depths and velocities in and around the building sufficiently low, such that the risk of structural damage to the building (due to scour, impact loading etc) is acceptable?	
Are appropriate measures in place to prevent inappropriate use and later development of floors below flood level?	
Will the proposals be acceptable to the insurance industry?	

[1] The development is unlikely to be acceptable if the answer to any of these questions is "No".

A3.3.4   Land raising

A method which is frequently used to manage flood risk to a development is to raise land levels from existing ground levels to a level above the flood defence level, and to construct the development on this raised ground. Land raising schemes should not produce an area of land that would become an island during a flood event, and safe access to and from the development during the design flood event must be provided (Figure A3.2).

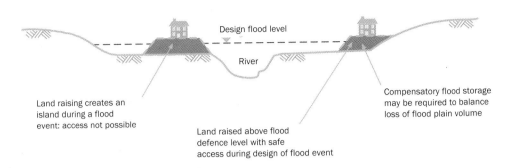

UNACCEPTABLE   ACCEPTABLE

Design flood level

River

Land raising creates an
island during a flood
event: access not possible

Land raised above flood
defence level with safe
access during design of flood event

Compensatory flood storage
may be required to balance
loss of flood plain volume

Figure A3.2   *Land raising*

Land raising is preferable to construction of flood defences for several reasons:

1   Following land raising, the development will be located outside the flood risk zone. This should facilitate the provision of insurance/mortgages, which would be less certain for developments located within the flood plain.

2   Flood depths in the development during a flood event which exceeds the flood defence level will be lower on raised ground than in a development located behind a flood defence (Figure A3.3).

3   The likelihood and consequences of erosion of raised ground are lower than for breaching of flood defences.

4   The flood defence maintenance requirements associated with developments on raised ground are lower than those associated with flood defences.

5   Provision of drainage for developments on raised ground is simpler than for developments behind flood defences, as the drainage system is less likely to become tidelocked.

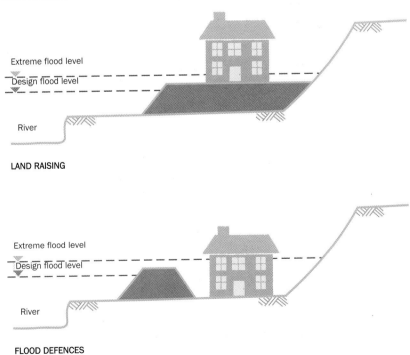

Extreme flood level
Design flood level

River

LAND RAISING

Extreme flood level
Design flood level

River

FLOOD DEFENCES

Figure A3.3   *Potential flood depths in a development during an extreme event, demonstrating the benefits of land raising compared to flood defences*

The velocity of flood water in the area to be raised, both before and after land raising should be ascertained, and the potential for erosion of the raised land assessed. If necessary, appropriate erosion protection measures should be employed (May *et al*, 2002).

A disadvantage of land raising is that it may require large volumes of fill and substantial earthworks to raise the development to the required level, and this may have to be imported on to the site if suitable material cannot be won locally. Land raising may not be a viable option if existing buildings or other features that are to be retained are located at existing ground level.

Other factors that may affect the feasibility of land raising include the availability of suitable fill, potential environmental impacts and landscape issues. Potential settlement due to existing ground conditions and the nature of the fill should also be taken into account. These factors will typically be beyond the scope of an FRA, but should be considered at an early stage to ensure the feasibility of the proposals.

Any proposal to raise land within the flood plain to protect the new development from flooding is likely to be associated with the need for appropriate compensatory flood plain storage measures to avoid increasing the flood risk downstream (Appendix A3.3.10). If the land raising is to occur within the area of flood plain conveying flow, appropriate measures should be undertaken to avoid an unacceptable increase in upstream water levels.

Table A3.5 provides a checklist that, together with Table A3.2, should assist in deciding whether a proposed land raising scheme is appropriate.

Table A3.5 *Key considerations for the design of land raising measures*

Consideration	YES/NO[1]
Is it feasible to raise the land to above flood defence level?	
Is safe access to and from the raised area possible during the design flood event?	
Has it been demonstrated that the proposed land raising will not increase upstream water levels?	
Has it been demonstrated that any potential loss of flood storage caused by the land raising will be adequately compensated?	
Has the erosion risk to the raised land been assessed, and are appropriate measures planned to manage this risk?	
Are the environmental and geotechnical impacts of the proposed land raising acceptable?	

[1] The development is unlikely to be acceptable if the answer to any of these questions is "No".

A3.3.5   Flood warning

The majority of new developments should be designed so that flood warning is not a necessary part of the development design. Even so, the use of warning signs highlighting the susceptibility of an area to flood is recommended in areas which are subject to flood risk and where the public has access. Evacuation routes to be used in the event of a flood should also be clearly signed, and marking used to identify such routes should be clearly visible during a flood event.

Flood warning may be a useful mitigation measure for managing flood risk when extreme events which exceed the design flood event occur, and may be needed in conjunction with other mitigation measures. The need for, and feasibility of, flood warning systems for a development should be discussed with the FDA.

A3.3.6

Flood proofing

Flood proofing is a technique whereby buildings are designed to withstand the effects of flooding. Flood proofing is unlikely to be suitable as the only mitigation measure for most new residential developments, but may be suitable in certain circumstances (Box A3.2)

Box A3.2 *Types of development where flood proofing may be appropriate*

- industrial developments where temporary disruption is acceptable
- developments which are designed with ground floors that can flood (Appendix A3.3.3)
- developments where the use of an existing building is to be changed
- developments which include basements that are at risk of flooding (see CIRIA, 1995)
- developments which are located on the edge of the flood risk zone, such that flooding depths are likely to be very low and access may be maintained during a flood event
- developments which will not flood during the design flood event, but which may be flooded by an extreme flood event.

Flood proofing methods fall into two main categories:

1 **Dry proofing** methods are designed to keep water out of the building, and can include design of floors and walls to withstand water pressures and prevent seepage (passive measures) and the provision of temporary covers on openings in walls (active measures).

2 **Wet proofing** methods are designed to improve the ability of the property to withstand the effects of flooding once water has entered the building, and can include construction with appropriate materials, use of flood-resistant fittings and locating vulnerable services above design flood level.

Flood proofing techniques can be applied to a number of permanent features within a building and, if properly designed, can substantially reduce the impact of flooding on the building. Guidance on the detailed consideration of building design and materials that can be used to improve flood proofing are given in a variety of references (ODPM, 2002; American Society of Civil Engineers, 1998; Building Research Establishment Scottish Laboratory, 1996). May *et al*, (1998)) provide information on anti-flooding devices that can prevent backflow up drainage systems, such as flap valves and pumping systems.
A summary of some of the recommendations given in current guidance is given in Table A3.6.

Table A3.6 *A selection of recommendations for flood proofing measures which can be incorporated within the design of buildings (subject to compliance with Building Regulations)*

Feature	Considerations to improve flood proofing
External walls	Careful consideration of materials: use low permeability materials to limit water penetration if dry proofing required. Avoid using timber frame and cavity walls. Consider applying a water resistant coating. Provide fittings for flood boards or other temporary barriers across openings in the walls (dry proofing).
Internal walls	Avoid use of gypsum plaster and plasterboard; use more flood resistant linings (eg hydraulic lime, ceramic tiles). Avoid use of stud partition walls.
Floors	Avoid use of chipboard floors. Use concrete floors with integrated and continuous damp proof membrane and damp proof course. Solid concrete floors are preferable; if a suspended floor is to be used, provide facility for drainage of sub-floor void. Use solid insulation materials.
Fitting, fixtures and services	If possible, locate all fittings, fixtures and services above design flood level. Avoid chipboard and MDF. Consider use of removable plastic fittings. Use solid doors treated with waterproof coatings. Avoid using double-glazed window units that may fill with flood water. Use solid wood staircases. Avoid fitted carpets. Locate electrical, gas and telephone equipment and systems above design flood level. Fit anti-flooding devices to drainage systems.

Dry proofing techniques should not be used unless the building is able to withstand the differential pressures across load-bearing walls and the flotation effects that will occur during flood events. For most existing properties this will mean that dry flood proofing should not be used if the expected flood depth is over 0.9 m (ODPM, 2002).

Even where dry proofing is proposed, it is recommended that wet proofing is also incorporated into the development design, in case of failure of the dry proofing provisions.

Active flood proofing techniques include the provision of items such as flood boards, flood gates and air brick covers, and there is a wide range of products available. A scheme is now in place to award satisfactory active flood proofing products a British Standards Institution (BSI) Kitemark. It is recommended that only BSI approved products are used to provide active flood proofing. It is important that active flood proofing measures can be returned to their normal state as quickly as possible following a flood event so that normal operation can be resumed. Developments that rely on active flood proofing measures will require some form of flood warning system (Appendix A3.3.5). Active flood proofing measures are only likely to be acceptable in commercial and industrial premises, where a permanent workforce is available to install the systems within the flood warning lead time.

When assessing the feasibility of wet proofing methods it is important that sufficient warning time and access is provided to allow evacuation of the area and the movement of sensitive assets to above flood level before flooding. A flood response plan should be prepared and practised regularly. The building and any contents that cannot be easily moved to above design flood level, must be designed to withstand immersion in flood water or be designed to be easily replaceable. It is important that the potential effects of poor water quality be assessed. Flood water is often polluted with chemicals, including sewage, and pollution can have long-lasting health and safety effects (Section 3.2.4). Wet proofing should be considered only if the expected frequency and duration of disruption due to flooding and associated clean up operations is acceptable.

Design of flood proofing measures should conform to the relevant Building Regulations/Standards.

APPENDIX A3

If flood proofing measures are to be incorporated into the design of a development it is essential that future owners/occupiers/operators are aware of the flood risk and the nature of the flood proofing measures.

It is essential that the building is designed to withstand possible scour and debris impacts. For this reason flood proofing is unlikely to be feasible if flood velocities are high.

If a property is protected by dry proofing then compensatory flood storage works will be required to replace the storage volume lost due to the exclusion of flood water from within the property (Appendix A3.3.10). As wet proofing allows water within the property, compensatory flood storage may not be required.

Table A3.7 provides a checklist that, together with Table A3.2, should assist in deciding whether flood proofing is likely to be applicable for a development.

Table A3.7 *Key considerations for the design of flood proofing measures*

Consideration	YES/NO[1]
Is the development type suitable for flood proofing? (Box A3.2)	
Is the building capable of withstanding the depth and velocity of flooding?	
Can all the vulnerable contents, fixtures and fittings be located above flood level?	
Would the disruption caused by flooding within the building be acceptable?	
Will the frequency and duration of disruption be acceptable?	
Can flood proofing be achieved using wholly passive systems? If, not will a flood warning system be provided and will a permanent workforce be available to install active systems within the flood warning lead time?	
If dryproofing is to be used, can adequate compensatory flood plain storage be provided?	
Will flood proofing measures be acceptable to the FDA and insurance industry?	
Have arrangements been proposed to ensure that future users of the development are aware of the flood risk and the flood proofing methods to be employed?	
Would evacuation and access arrangements during a flood event be adequate?	

[1] The development is unlikely to be acceptable if the answer to any of these questions is "No".

A3.3.7 Design of channel and hydraulic structures

The design of channel and hydraulic structures as a mitigation measure can be split into three categories:

- definition of acceptable development encroachment;
- correct design of bridge/culvert crossings;
- modifications to existing flood channels to offset the impacts of a development.

Acceptable development encroachment

The preferred method of avoiding an unacceptable increase in upstream water levels due to a development is to limit the extent of development within the area of flood plain conveying flow (Figure A3.4). Using hydraulic modelling (Appendix A2.3.1) it is possible to determine the extent to which the development could encroach into the flood plain without water levels rising by more than the amount permitted by the LPA/FDA (Section 5.2).

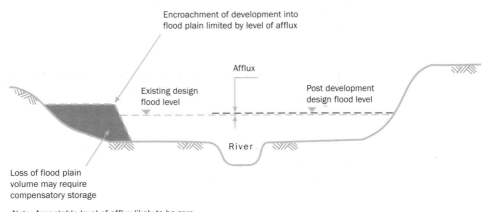

Figure A3.4 *Impact of development encroachment*

If the development is to encroach into the flood plain to such an extent that it may cause unacceptable increases in upstream water levels then modifications to the channel may be an option to offset this impact (see below).

Design of culvert crossings

Culverting of watercourses should be avoided wherever possible as construction of culverts may affect the ecology of the watercourse and may increase flood risk. Both the Environment Agency and SEPA have general policies against culverting of watercourses. Wherever possible, bridge crossings should be used in preference to culverts. If culverting of a watercourse or flood flow route is unavoidable then several requirements should typically be met (Box A3.3).

Box A3.3 *Key requirements for culvert crossings (after Environment Agency, 1999b)*

- the culvert should be sufficiently large that it will not cause an unacceptable afflux
- exit velocities should be sufficiently low that erosion will not occur, unless appropriate scour protection is provided to above design flood level.
- culverts should typically be designed with an invert level set below natural bed levels and a bed of natural material should be provided
- the soffit of the culvert should have sufficient freeboard above design flood level
- careful consideration should be given to the risk of blockage and the corresponding inspection and maintenance requirements; appropriate access should be provided for maintenance and cleaning. If necessary, appropriately designed trash screens should be provided
- careful consideration should be given to the safety issues related to the culvert

The culvert should be designed so that any increase in water levels upstream of the crossing will be less than the amount permitted by the FDA/LPA (Section 5.2), for a range of flood events up to and including the design flood event.

Potential velocities through the culvert and at the culvert entrance and exit should be investigated and the possible effects of scour assessed. If necessary, appropriate scour protection measures should be included within the design. Ramsbottom *et al*, (1997) and May *et al*, (2002) provide advice on how to address these issues. If practicable, velocities through the culvert should be restricted so that natural bed material can be used within the culvert. This requires the culvert invert to be set below existing bed level, with the natural material being used to raise the bed level up to natural bed level.

Consideration should be given to the risk of blockage of the culvert. The soffit of the culvert should be sufficiently far above flood level so that the risk of the accumulation of debris at the entrance to and within the culvert is low. If a trash screen is required this should be designed in accordance with Ramsbottom *et al*, (1997), and Environment Agency (2002) unless the FDA has any local guidance which may supersede this. Trash screens should be provided only following careful consideration of the potential advantages and disadvantages.

Culverts have the potential to pose significant health and safety hazards, and this should be carefully considered. If the situation requires security screen to prevent access into the culvert (notably by children) it should be recognised that such a screen will almost certainly collect debris. If a security screen is required on the downstream end of a culvert a trash screen will be required on the upstream end.

The key design parameters (invert level, soffit level, freeboard etc) and maintenance responsibilities (duties, responsible parties, frequency etc) associated with any culverts and screens should be agreed with the FDA.

Assessment of the adequacy of culvert design will require hydrological and hydraulic modelling. Most hydraulic modelling packages include units that can model the hydraulic behaviour of culverts. Ramsbottom *et al*, (1997) and Environment Agency (1999b) provide more information on the appropriate design of culverts. Manufacturers' guides for culvert capacities should not be used to determine culvert capacity in FRAs, as these typically refer to full pipe flow and ignore the effects of inlet and outlet losses.

Design of bridge crossings

When designing bridge crossings across watercourses and other flood flow routes several requirements should typically be met (Box A3.4 and Figure A3.5).

Box A3.4   *Key requirements for bridge crossings* (after Environment Agency, 1999c)

- wherever practicable, the bridge should have a clear span over the watercourse channel
- the bridge crossing should not cause an unacceptable increase in upstream water level (afflux)
- exit velocities should be sufficiently low that erosion will not occur, unless appropriate scour protection is provided to above design flood level.
- bridge foundations should be designed so that they are not vulnerable to scour effects
- the soffit of the bridge should have sufficient freeboard above design flood level
- the bridge crossing should not restrict maintenance access to the watercourse.

New watercourse crossings should have openings for the main channel and also in areas where significant velocities occur on the flood plain. These openings should be positioned and sized to ensure that any increase in water levels upstream of the crossing will be less than the maximum amount specified by the FDA/LPA (Section 5.2), for a range of flood events up to and including the design flood event. Ideally, the bridge across the main channel should be a clear span, so that there are no piers within the main channel to obstruct flows or collect debris. The main bridge opening should be sufficiently wide to allow maintenance access (Appendix A2.1.2) next to the watercourse on at least one bank.

Potential velocities through the bridge should be investigated and the possible effects of scour assessed. If necessary, appropriate scour protection measures should be included within the design. May *et al*, (2002) provide advice on how to address these issues.

The soffit of the bridge should be sufficiently far above flood level so that the risk of the bridge deck being struck by debris is low. Minimum freeboard requirements for bridge soffits are typically between 0.6 m and 1 m.

Further guidance on design requirements for bridges can be found in Environment Agency (1999b). Requirements for freeboard and other parameters for individual bridges should be agreed with the FDA.

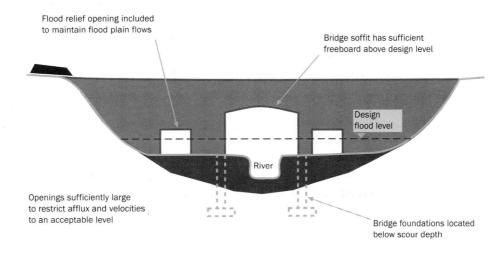

Figure A3.5   *Key features of a well designed bridge*

Assessment of the adequacy of bridge design will require hydrological and hydraulic modelling. Most hydraulic modelling packages include units that can model the hydraulic behaviour of bridges, although the units used should be selected carefully to match the characteristics of the bridge. Highways Agency (1995) provide guidance on how to estimate afflux due to bridge crossings.

Channel modifications

The design flood level is a function of the flood flow and the conveyance capacity of the channel/flood plain system. If channel modifications are undertaken to increase the conveyance capacity of the channel, then flood levels at the site – and for some distance upstream – can be reduced, although this will result in a reduction of flood storage. Channel modifications will also be required if a culvert is to be removed and replaced with an open channel, and can be undertaken to improve drainage routes around a development (eg to deal with overland flow or groundwater flooding). Channel enlargements may be undertaken in tidally affected watercourses (on the inland side of tidal gates), or on watercourses which require pumping, to increase the storage capacity within the watercourse.

Channel modifications should be undertaken only if no other method of reducing upstream water levels is practicable, or if they are being undertaken to provide environmental enhancement. This is because channel modifications can be associated with significant problems, including:

- **environmental impacts:** disruption of the fluvial and riparian environment during construction and, if inappropriately designed, during operation

- **downstream impacts:** increasing channel conveyance can increase flood flows downstream; this may lead to the need to provide compensatory storage works to reduce downstream flood flows back to current levels

- **maintenance requirements:** ongoing maintenance requirements may arise from channel modification works as changes to the channel characteristics can cause erosion and sedimentation problems

- **construction and consenting requirements:** working within the watercourse channel can lead to constraints on construction practices and timescales and the need to obtain relevant consents from the FDA (Appendix A1)

- **cost:** the above factors mean that channel modification can be a costly exercise.

If channel modifications are to be undertaken then the conveyance capacity of a channel could be increased in a number of ways:

- **reduce roughness:** replacement of existing natural substrate with a smoother alternative (eg concrete)

- **straighten the channel:** increase the hydraulic gradient by reducing the length of the watercourse channel

- **enlarge the channel:** obtain a larger cross-sectional area, by widening or deepening the channel, and producing a more regular cross-section.

In the past the first two options for modifying channels were commonly undertaken. However, experience has shown that in addition to damaging the environment, these techniques often produce only short-term improvements, as the watercourse readjusts back to its original form, unless significant expenditure of maintenance is committed. These techniques are therefore not recommended.

The most environmentally sustainable form of channel enlargement will usually be a multi-stage channel. In this design the main channel is retained at a size appropriate for low to medium flows, with a berm or flood relief channel being provided which is designed to carry flood flows. The main channel can be designed with appropriate features typical of natural channels in the area. Berms or flood relief channels can be designed to add environmental benefit to the area.

The behaviour of a multi-stage channel scheme should be modelled for a range of flows up to and including the design flood flow. In complex situations physical modelling may be required to ensure that the proposed modifications will have the desired effect.

The impact of channel modifications on downstream flood flows should be assessed and, if necessary, compensatory works should be provided downstream to mitigate for any potential increase.

Careful consideration should be given to the potential effects of the proposals on fluvial geomorphology, including the potential for erosion of the newly constructed channel prior to establishment of vegetation and the potential for long-term sedimentation. Responsibilities for the maintenance of a modified channel should be agreed.

Further details on the design of two-stage channels is given in Ward *et al,* (1994).

If increasing the conveyance of the channel is not practical then it may be possible to construct a flood relief channel around the development (Fisher & Ramsbottom, 2001). This involves constructing a new channel which will carry flood flows from upstream of the development, around and back into the watercourse further downstream, effectively bypassing the development. This will be achievable only where the topography allows this to be done. In addition to the problems listed above for channel enlargement this technique will also require the purchase of significant areas of land outside of the development boundary. For this reason it is unlikely to be viable for most developments.

Table A3.8 provides a checklist that, together with Table A3.2, should assist in deciding whether proposed channel improvements or bridge/culvert crossings are appropriate.

Table A3.8   *Key considerations for schemes involving channel improvements and bridge/culvert crossings*

Consideration	YES/NO[1]
Can it be shown that the works do not lead to unacceptable water levels upstream of and next to the works?	
Will the flood velocities following the scheme be such that erosion will not occur or can be managed?	
Can it be shown that the works do not lead to an increase in downstream flood risk?	
Are the works designed such that the risk of disruption due to debris or sedimentation is acceptable?	
Have appropriate maintenance arrangements been made for the life of the development?	
Are the environmental and geomorphological impacts of the proposed works acceptable?	
Would the proposed works be consistent with the strategic flood management policies of the FDA?	
Will the relevant consents be given by the FDA?	
Have the works been designed so as to manage health and safety risks?	

[1] The development is unlikely to be acceptable if the answer to any of these questions is "No".

A3.3.8   Flood defences

In principle, flood defences can be constructed to protect a development from the design flood. This may involve upgrading or replacing existing flood defences, or the construction of new flood defences in previously undefended areas.

The construction of new flood defences to facilitate development within the flood risk zone should be avoided where possible. As noted in DTLR (2001) "…as part of its strategy for sustainable development, the government wishes to avoid an unnecessary increase in the requirement to provide artificial defence against flooding."

Construction of new structural flood defence measures for developments may not be sustainable in the long-term, as such defences are associated with ongoing maintenance requirements and risk of failure. Flood defences may also disturb aquatic and riparian habitats, have adverse visual impacts, and can restrict access to riverbanks. In addition, drainage of local runoff from behind flood defences can be problematic during flood events. As flood defences must tie into high ground or existing flood defences, it may be necessary to construct flood defences in areas outside the development site itself.

Therefore, flood defences are not a desirable means of managing flood risk to new developments, unless they provide benefit to existing developments currently at risk of flooding.

Flood defences for new developments should not be proposed unless it is agreed with the FDA that the proposed flood defences do not conflict with any strategic flood management plans that the FDA may have for the area.

Flood defences can be classified as permanent, demountable and temporary (Ogunyoye and van Heereveld, 2002). It is not acceptable to propose a flood defence strategy that relies on temporary measures (such as sandbags) as part of a new development.

Demountable defences are sometimes used to protect existing infrastructure. These consist of permanent below ground structures, with a removable above ground structure which can be closed or put in place when a flood warning is received. Demountable defences are associated with the major drawback that if they are not erected in time, the defence will fail and flooding will occur. For demountable defences to be viable it is essential that the development has both an adequate flood warning system (Appendix A3.3.5) and a nominated workforce responsible for closure of the systems. For this reason demountable defences are unlikely to be an acceptable mitigation measure for a new development, unless they are solely included to provide mitigation in the case of an extreme event or defence failure.

Permanent flood defences usually consist of walls or embankments, or a combination of the two (Figure A3.6).

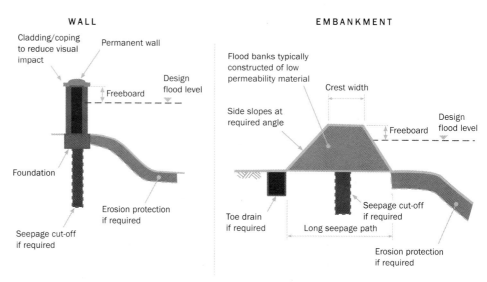

Figure A3.6   *Typical arrangements for permanent flood defences (after Ogunyoye and van Heereveld, 2002).*

Embankments can have a lower visual impact than flood walls, but the land take associated with flood embankments is greater than with walls. In both types of structure it is important to ensure that the structure will be stable, not susceptible to internal failure (eg piping in flood embankments), and that seepage rates through and under the structures will be acceptable. In permeable soils it may be necessary to install seepage cut-offs below the defences and pressure relief drains on the landward side of the defences.

The design of flood embankment crest width and sideslopes will depend upon the material of which the embankment is constructed, seepage path length required and on maintenance requirements. Small embankments which are to be maintained by hand should typically have minimum crest widths of 2 m and maximum sideslopes of 1 (vertical) in 2 (horizontal). Larger flood embankments should have minimum crest widths of 4 m and maximum sideslopes of 1 (vertical) in 2.5 (horizontal) to allow access by maintenance vehicles.

It is essential that access for maintenance is available for both flood embankments and walls. Responsibility for the future maintenance of flood defences should be agreed with the FDA. Shrubs and trees should not be planted on flood embankments as their roots can lead to enhanced seepage and piping failure, and will encourage the presence of burrowing animals. Animal burrows have led to the failure of flood defence embankments. These should be maintained with a cover of short grass.

It should be ensured that the flood defence will withstand future scour effects and, if necessary, appropriate scour protection should be placed in front of the flood defence (see May *et al*, 2002).

Any drain, sewer or watercourse which will drain through the flood defences should be fitted with a flap valve and/or penstock. The potential failure of such non-return valves should be assessed (Appendix A2.2.8) and back-up sluices together with measures for dealing with tidelocked surface water (Section 2.2.3) should be provided where appropriate.

Whenever new flood defences are constructed it is necessary to consider the impacts of the potential failure or overtopping of the defences, including provision for drainage of flood water from the development area. The construction of flood defences may lead to a reduction in the availability of flood storage, and compensatory flood storage works (Appendix A3.3.10) may therefore need to be provided.

Table A3.9 gives a checklist that, together with Table A3.2, may assist in deciding whether proposed flood defences may be acceptable

Table A3.9   *Key considerations for flood defences*

Consideration	YES/NO[1]
Can it be demonstrated that there is no practicable alternative to flood defences?	
Are the proposed defences replacing/upgrading existing defences, and/or will the flood defences be consistent with the strategic flood management policies of the FDA?	
Has the FDA indicated that defences may be acceptable, given the situation?	
Will the proposed defence provide the required standard of protection over the life of the development?	
Will the proposed defence prevent unacceptable seepage?	
Have arrangements been proposed for dealing with any drains or watercourses passing through or beneath the defence?	
Have the consequences of defence overtopping and breaching been considered, and have appropriate mitigation measures been proposed?	
Is there adequate provision for maintenance access to the defence and any watercourses?	
Can it be shown that proposals will not lead to an increase in flood risk elsewhere?	
Are the environmental impacts of the proposed works acceptable?	
Can the defence be constructed wholly on the development site, or on land which can be purchased for the purposes of constructing the defence?	
Have arrangements been made for the maintenance of the defence over the lifetime of the development?	
If any demountable defences are proposed, has the design, maintenance and operation of these been agreed with the FDA?	
Will the relevant consents be awarded by the FDA?	

[1] The development is unlikely to be acceptable if the answer to any of these questions is "No".

A3.3.9   **Developer contributions to strategic flood risk management**

In some situations it may be possible for the developer of a site to contribute towards a planned flood alleviation scheme that is part of the long-term plan for strategic flood risk management of an area, rather than provide site-specific mitigation measures (Box A3.5). Such an option is worth consideration where the viability of undertaking site specific mitigation is limited, and where an existing flooding problem exists in the area, for which the FDA has an identified strategy.

Box A3.5   *Case history – developer contribution to strategic flood risk management*

A retail development was proposed next to a river close to a town centre with a history of flooding. Significant flooding of the town occurred in 1955 and 1960, when the river overtopped banks and walls in the town. The Environment Agency and its predecessor bodies had undertaken a number of studies into flood alleviation options between 1964 and 1990. When the new development was proposed the opportunity was taken to construct a flood alleviation scheme which would protect the development and improve the standard of protection for the town.

The flood alleviation scheme involved the creation of a flood storage reservoir upstream of the town, to attenuate flood flows and lower the 1 per cent flood level in the area of the retail site. This would also lead to a reduction in flood levels throughout the town. An embankment was raised across the flood plain of the river to create a flood storage reservoir and a culvert used to restrict downstream flows. The reservoir was designed to safely pass events in excess of the 1 per cent flood without failure, in accordance with the Reservoirs Act (1975). The flood alleviation scheme also allowed for improved management of Sites of Special Scientific Interest (SSSIs) in the area.

As the scheme provided strategic benefits to flood management for a wider area than the development site itself, the Environment Agency agreed to take responsibility for its operation and maintenance. The developer was responsible for implementing the design and construction of the scheme to the satisfaction of the EA.

In these cases, it may be more cost effective for the developer to assist in the implementation of a strategic flood alleviation scheme than to carry out mitigation measures for the development site alone. This may be beneficial to all parties as the development will, in effect, reduce overall flood risk. For this reason, the FDA may be prepared to assume responsibility for the operation and maintenance of such schemes.

The planning of such schemes will require close consultation with the FDA, including discussions about the mitigation measures required to ensure that the proposed development itself is adequately protected.

In this context flood alleviation schemes, which developers may become involved in, could include a variety of flood mitigation measures and may include any of the following:

- improving the condition and/or height of flood defences (Appendix A3.3.8)

- construction of new on- or off-site flood defences (Appendix A3.3.8), which will provide flood protection benefit to other properties in the area – not just the proposed development

- construction or upgrading of a pumping station (Appendix A3.3.12), which will provide flood protection benefit to other properties in the area – not just the proposed development

- undertaking channel improvements and/or removing restrictions to flow (Appendix A3.3.7), including replacement of culverts with open channels

- provision of upstream storage

- river restoration.

Upstream storage areas reduce flood risk by storing flood water during the peak of a flood event and releasing it gradually at a lower rate, effectively acting as an engineered form of flood plain storage (Figure 2.4). Upstream storage works are attractive as they can mitigate for the whole range of potential development impacts, and can provide extensive benefits downstream of the storage area. The storage areas themselves may also be used to provide amenity or environmental benefits. More detailed guidance on the design of upstream storage areas is provided in Hall *et al*, (1993).

An alternative method of increasing upstream storage without the need for an impounding structure and flow control device is river and flood plain restoration. In locations where engineered channels are located upstream of a development it may be possible to reduce flood flows by restoring the watercourse channel to a more natural meandering course. In certain areas it may also be possible to remove flood embankments protecting agricultural areas to allow larger areas to flood. This will increase water levels and the storage of water on the flood plain in the restored section, reducing downstream flood flows (Acreman, 2003). Techniques for restoring river and flood plain systems are described in River Restoration Centre (2002).

A3.3.10   Compensatory flood storage

Compensatory flood storage works are required where the proposed development would otherwise reduce the available volume of flood storage.

Compensatory flood storage must become effective at the same point in a flood event as the lost storage would have done (McPherson, 2002). It should therefore provide the same volume, and be at the same level relative to flood level, as the lost storage. This requirement is often referred to as "level for level" or "direct" compensation.

If the compensatory storage is provided at another level it will already be full (if lower) or still be empty (if higher), when the storage is required, and the characteristics of flood storage at this location will, therefore, be altered.

Ideally, the compensatory storage should be created immediately next to the location of the development. Upstream sites may also be effective, providing that no major inflow occurs between the development and the compensatory flood storage site. For many developments it is likely that suitable land will not be available for the provision of compensatory flood storage within the boundary of the development site, so alternative sites will have to be identified. This may lead to land identification and purchase problems.

Compensatory flood storage may be provided either by direct or indirect replacement of flood storage (Box A3.6), as described below. Direct "level for level" storage is the preferred means of compensatory flood storage provision.

Box A3.6   *Direct and indirect replacement of flood storage*

Direct replacement replaces the storage lost due to the development at the same level as it is lost. This ensures that the storage is filled at the same time during a flood event as it would have done under existing conditions.

Indirect replacement replaces the lost storage at a different level to that at which it is lost, although flow into the compensatory storage area is controlled with the objective of filling the storage at the same rate during a flood event as would have occurred under existing conditions.

Direct replacement of flood storage

Direct replacement of flood storage is achieved by regrading land to a lower level in order to replace the volume lost due to the development (Figure A3.7).

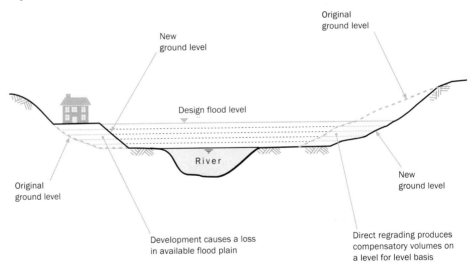

Figure A3.7   *Direct replacement of flood storage*

In order to design the compensatory flood storage scheme it is first necessary to calculate the potential loss of flood storage due to the proposed development. Losses of flood storage volume should typically be calculated for level bands so that at least five level bands represent the depth of flooding on the flood plain during the design flood, although level bands of less than 100 mm should not normally be used. The number of slices required will depend on the required volume of compensatory storage relative to total flood volume. The thickness of slice to be used should be agreed with the FDA.

Once the loss of flood volume has been calculated, land regrading works can be designed to provide a comparable amount of new storage for each level band. If compensatory flood storage is to be provided at a different location along the watercourse from that where the development is located, then water levels at the replacement site will be different from those at the development site. If that is the case, flood storage volumes should be attributed to flow bands rather than level bands, and replacement storage recreated at the equivalent flows at the replacement site.

When such a scheme is designed it is important that the form of the regraded land is such that the existing pattern of flow from the watercourse to the flood plain, and drainage of the land following a flood event, is maintained.

The feasibility of a direct level for level replacement scheme is dependent on a number of factors. The primary factor is the topography, as sufficient areas of land at a suitable level must be available. If the existing land surface is too low then inundation will occur too early, and level for level storage will not be possible. If the existing land is too high then excessive amounts of overburden will need to be excavated to produce the required landform, and the works may also significantly increase the total area of land subject to flood risk. The ability of a developer to find and use appropriate land at the required level is often a major obstacle to the feasibility of providing compensatory flood storage at a site. If such an area is available, it may be more cost-effective to consider development relocation (Appendix A3.3.1) or zoning (Appendix A3.3.2) in this area than to undertake land raising and subsequent compensatory flood storage works.

It is important that land lowering associated with a compensation scheme does not increase flood risk to other areas or properties. Other factors such as ecology, landscape and visual impacts, archaeology, services and land ownership, can affect the feasibility of such schemes. Excavation operations within flood risk areas are associated with the risk of high sediment loads entering watercourses and can be difficult to perform in wet weather conditions. Public safety should also be considered.

Potential exists when performing a direct replacement operation to provide ecological benefit to areas, through the construction of new habitats, such as wetlands and wader scrapes.

Table A3.10 provides a checklist that, together with Table A3.2, should assist in deciding on the likely acceptability of for a level for level compensatory flood storage scheme.

Table A3.10   *Key considerations for direct level for level compensatory storage schemes*

Consideration	YES/NO[1]
Has an appropriate area of land for compensatory flood storage works been identified, and is it available to the developer for this use?	
Has the volume of storage potentially lost due to the development been appropriately calculated?	
Do calculations show that direct "level for level" compensatory storage works can be designed to ensure no net loss of storage at any level of flooding up to and including the design flood event?	
Do the proposed works maintain the pattern of flooding and drainage on the flood plain?	
Are the environmental impacts of the proposed works acceptable?	
Will the relevant consents be awarded by the FDA?	

[1] The development is unlikely to be acceptable if the answer to any of these questions is "No".

Indirect replacement of flood storage

Where direct replacement is not practicable it may be possible to provide indirect compensatory flood storage, if the FDA accept that the development is necessary and that there is no other reasonable alternative. In certain situations it may be possible to provide a combined scheme, with both direct and indirect compensatory storage being provided.

Indirect replacement may be provided through the use of a protected area into which water is allowed to spill at a controlled rate. This is typically an area of excavated land surrounded by a flood embankment with an inflow restriction device (eg weir or gate) incorporated into it. Water is prevented from flowing into this area until the flood reaches the level at which additional compensatory storage is required, at which time the water is allowed to flow into the bunded area at a controlled rate to mimic the natural rate at which the flood plain would fill. A controlled outfall (typically a culvert with flap valve or gate) is provided to allow water from the bunded area to drain out as the water level in the watercourse falls.

Schemes involving indirect replacement of flood storage are more problematic to design and operate than those involving direct replacement of storage and should only be considered where it has been shown that it is not feasible to provide direct replacement of flood storage, and where the FDA accepts that such a scheme may be practicable. Indirect replacement of flood storage is less satisfactory than direct replacement for the following reasons:

- the rate of inflow into storage is designed based on a design hydrograph; unlike a direct replacement scheme, the efficiency of the storage area will be sensitive to flood hydrograph shape and multiple events

- indirect storage provision requires the flow of water into and out of the compensatory storage area to be controlled. This leads to the requirement for control structures and devices

- control devices will usually be associated with the use of moving parts and are therefore associated with ongoing operational and maintenance requirements

- there is a risk of failure of the flow control devices (eg because of blockage or jamming), which could lead to failure of the storage area to fill in the required manner during a flood event, especially if adequate maintenance is not undertaken

Because of the reasons above, indirect storage schemes are usually more expensive than level for level storage schemes.

As these schemes typically include excavations which may fill rapidly with water, they may be associated with significant health and safety risks.

It is unlikely that the FDA will accept proposals incorporating indirect replacement of flood storage, unless the development has a long-term operation and maintenance arrangement associated with it, and the scheme can be shown to produce environmental benefits. There is a general presumption against the use of indirect compensatory storage schemes and any proposals associated with such a scheme should be discussed with the FDA.

A3.3.11 Management of development runoff

Careful design of runoff from the development site is required, both to manage the flood risk posed on the site due to runoff and to avoid an increase in flood risk downstream of the site. Long-term operation and maintenance requirements and responsibilities are a key consideration with runoff management techniques and may have a major influence on the choice of methods.

Attenuation of runoff from development sites is required to avoid an increase in runoff rates and volumes in receiving watercourses (Section 3.3.2). Consideration should be given to the means of providing flow attenuation at the development site at an early stage of site planning as this can influence site masterplanning. The feasibility of managing development runoff may constrain the extent of land that may be developed, and runoff management measures may be used as landscaping features.

Where developments discharge directly into watercourses which are subject to tidelocking it may be more appropriate to provide on-line attenuation through increasing the storage capacity of the receiving watercourse (Appendix A3.3.7) than providing on-site attenuation, as flood risk is influenced by both rainfall and tidal events (Section 2.2.3). In such cases every effort should still be made to encourage infiltration to minimise development runoff at source.

Attenuation of flows from development sites has been undertaken for many years, and there is a wealth of available literature relating to the design of such mitigation measures. Attenuation can be achieved either by Sustainable Drainage Systems (SUDS) or through more traditional means (oversized pipes, tanks etc). SUDS techniques (Martin *et al*, 2000a; 2000b; 2001) are preferred to traditional measures to control runoff as they attempt to reproduce the natural systems that govern runoff volumes and rates (Figure A3.8). They are more likely to manage the surface water quality problems which may be associated with development (Martin *et al*, 2000a; 2000b). SUDS techniques can also provide landscape and amenity features, and can increase the ecological diversity of a site.

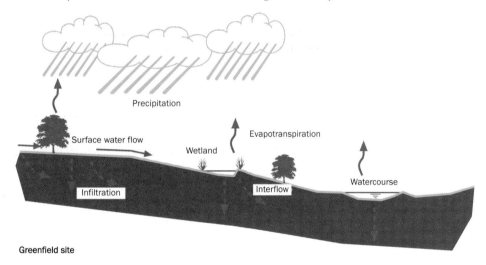

Greenfield site

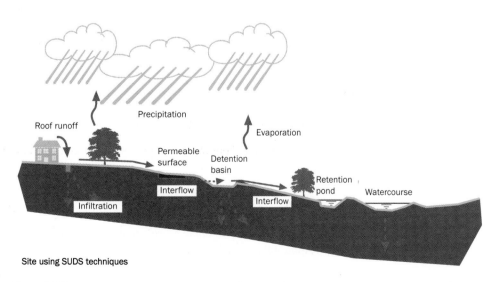

Site using SUDS techniques

Figure A3.8   *The hydrological cycle of a greenfield site and a site served by SUDS techniques* (after Martin *et al*, 2000b)

Whichever type of system is used, it should be designed so that the site drainage system will not cause flooding of the development during extreme events which exceed the design event, and so that the effectiveness of the system will not be compromised should a series of storm events occur.

SUDS techniques

There are a variety of SUDS techniques which may be used to control runoff, as described in more detail in Martin *et al*, (2000a; 2000b; 2001). All SUDS techniques have the added benefit that they can assist in the management of water quality, although the effectiveness of different techniques to do this varies.

Filter strips and swales are vegetated surface features that drain water evenly off impermeable areas, slowing and filtering the flow. Swales can be used to attenuate the flow, and infiltration may be possible from both types of device if ground conditions permit.

Filter drains and permeable surfaces are devices that have a volume of permeable material below ground to store surface water. These techniques can be used to attenuate flow and can be used as infiltration devices if ground conditions permit.

Infiltration devices drain water directly into the ground and include features such as soakaways, infiltration trenches and infiltration basins. They may be used at source or at the end of the surface water management train. The main function is to encourage infiltration of water into the ground, but they can also provide attenuation.

Basins and ponds (including wetlands) are areas where water can be stored on the surface. Basins are free from water during dry weather flow conditions, while ponds are permanently wet. They can be used for detention storage (attenuation) or retention (water quality treatment). If ground conditions permit they can be used as infiltration devices.

A variety of SUDS techniques are likely to be required for each development site. If possible infiltration techniques should be used to control runoff at its source.

Whilst SUDS should be implemented wherever possible, a number of limitations may be encountered when attempting to develop such a scheme, including:

- infiltration may not be possible if the permeability of the soil is limited or the water table is high

- infiltration may not be possible if groundwater vulnerability to pollution is high, or the site is located on contaminated land

- infiltration may not be possible if it could cause ground stability problems

- SUDS devices relying on infiltration or attenuation should not be located within the flood plain as their operation will be compromised during a flood event

- safety issues relating to the presence of surface water features should be considered

- SUDS devices relying on wetlands and surface water features may not be appropriate close to airports or below flight paths due to the risk of bird strike

- it may be difficult to obtain agreement on operation and maintenance responsibilities and adoption issues.

Consultation with the highways authority, FDA and drainage authority is likely to be required when determining the feasibility of providing SUDS techniques in development design.

Further guidance on the design of SUDS is provided by Martin *et al*, (2000a; 2000b; 2001) and Kellagher (2004). Consultation with the FDA/LPA is strongly recommended if SUDS systems are being considered.

Traditional techniques for surface water runoff

Where it is not possible to implement SUDS techniques at a site, or part of a site, traditional techniques may be implemented to manage surface water runoff. These techniques do not restrict the volume of water generated from the site or provide water quality treatment benefits, but can be used to attenuate peak flows to appropriate rates. Traditional methods of providing surface water runoff include:

- oversized pipes
- box culverts (used as buried water storage devices)
- tanks.

Further guidance on these techniques can be found in Kellagher (2004).

A3.3.12 Pumping

Where a development is to be protected by an existing or a new flood defence, pumping may be required to drain the low-lying area behind the defence, during periods when water levels within the receiving watercourse are higher than the maximum allowable water level within the development.

Typical situations in which pumping may be required include locations where:

- a watercourse drains through a flood defence and has a flap valve on its outfall
- surface water runoff may be trapped behind a flood defence, and where this may pose a flood risk to the development
- the development is at a lower level than a receiving carrier drain or sewer.

Wherever possible, development designs that are reliant on pumping should be avoided, as they have ongoing maintenance and running costs, and the development will be vulnerable should the pumping station fail. For this reason, developments that rely on pumping should be proposed only if the FDA accept that there is no alternative, and that the risks associated with pumping station failure can be managed. Developments that rely on pumping stations should be permitted only if key considerations are met (Table A3.11 and Table A3.2).

Table A3.11   *Considerations to be given when producing an outline design for a*
pumping station

Consideration	YES/NO[1]
Has it been shown that there is no practicable alternative arrangement that would allow gravity drainage to be achieved?	
Are the potential environmental impacts of pumping acceptable?	
Is the potential impact of pumping on downstream flood risk acceptable?	
Is the expected form, layout and appearance of the proposed pumping station acceptable?	
Are arrangements in place for the operation and maintenance of the pumping station for the lifetime of the development?	
Has the risk of potential failure of the pumping station been assessed, and have mitigation measures been implemented to manage this risk?	
Will the relevant consents be given by the FDA?	

[1] The development is unlikely to be acceptable if the answer to any of these questions is "No".

A4 Professional institutions

A flood risk assessment (FRA) should be undertaken by a competent professional. It is recommended that an FRA should be undertaken under the direction of a member of the relevant chartered professional institution, or equivalent, with experience of flood risk assessment and management.

The following institutions should be able to provide contact details of organisations that have the relevant experience to undertake FRAs. The FDA may also be able to recommend competent organisations.

INSTITUTION OF CIVIL ENGINEERS/BRITISH HYDROLOGICAL SOCIETY

The Institution of Civil Engineers (ICE) seeks to advance the knowledge, practice and business of civil engineering, and represents professionally qualified civil engineers.

The British Hydrological Society (BHS) an independent body that is formally associated with the Institution of Civil Engineers. The BHS maintains a register of consultants in hydrology that provides details of some of the organisations that are likely to be able to provide suitably qualified staff to undertake flood risk assessments. Advice can be found by contacting the secretary (see below) or through the Internet <www.hydrology.org.uk/BHS_Consultant_Register.html>.

The British Hydrological Society
Institution of Civil Engineers
1 Great George Street
London, SW1P 3AA
Tel. 0207 222 7722
Fax. 0207 222 7500
e-mail: bhs@ice.org.uk

CHARTERED INSTITUTION OF WATER AND ENVIRONMENTAL MANAGEMENT

The Chartered Institution of Water and Environmental Management (CIWEM) is an independent multi-disciplinary body for those committed to the sustainable management and development of water and the environment.

CIWEM maintain a professionals directory that includes contact details for consultants, contractors, manufacturers and suppliers in the environmental (water, air, or land) management sector. The professionals directory may be accessed on the Internet <www.ciwem.org.uk/directory/> and includes a large list of suppliers. The directory includes a variety of search terms, and those organisations listed under "flood defence" or "hydrology" are likely to be able to provide suitably qualified staff to undertake flood risk assessments.

Chartered Institution of Water and Environmental Management (CIWEM)
15 John Street
London WC1N 2EB
Tel: 020 7831 3110
Fax: 020 7405 4967
email: admin@ciwem.org.uk

APPENDIX A4

Summary risk register

A flood risk assessment (FRA) may involve a significant amount of work, may identify a number of issues and may lead to proposals for a range of measures to manage flood risk at a proposed development site. Many of these measures will rely on appropriate operation and maintenance regimes in the future to maintain their effectiveness. It would therefore be useful for those who will rely on the outcome of a FRA (ie those undertaking the detailed design, construction and maintenance/operation of the development) to have access to a simple summary of the issues relating to flooding on a development site. It is recommended that a risk register is included in each FRA report. This should summarise the flood risk issues at the site, the mitigation measures to be employed at the site to avoid an increase in flood risk, and the maintenance requirements associated with these mitigation measures.

An example of the format for a risk register that could be used in FRA reports is given below.

Description of risk/hazard	Mitigation measure proposed	Operation/maintenance requirement	Relevant section in FRA report for further information
Flooding of the development site, up to and including design flood event	Raise land above flood defence level	Annual inspection by management company required to ensure erosion of raised land is not occurring. Future owners/occupiers to be informed of reasons for and nature of the land raising.	
Flooding of the development site during extreme flood event	Buildings to be flood proofed to above extreme flood level	If any works are to be carried out on the buildings, management company to ensure that flood proofing is not compromised.	
Increase in upstream flood risk	A floodplain corridor is to be provided between the raised land and the river	No ground raising to be carried out within the floodplain corridor. Construction of any possible obstructions to flow (e.g. fences, hedges, outbuildings etc.) to be avoided in this area. Vegetation management to be undertaken to maintain short grass in this area.	
Increase in downstream flood risk (loss of flood plain storage)	The topography of the nature conservation area has been designed to compensate for the area and volume of flood plain lost due to the land raising.	No ground raising to be carried out within the nature conservation area. No modifications to be made to the nature conservation area which would affect the way in which water would enter or leave the area during a flood event. Responsible organisation to carry out maintenance in an appropriate manner to maintain ecological quality of area.	
Public safety in green space areas subject to flood risk	Warning signs erected to warn of dangers of flooding. Evacuation routes clearly marked.	Responsible organisation to ensure that warning signs and evacuation routes are maintained.	
All	Prepare operation & maintenance manual	Future owners/occupiers to be informed of reasons for and nature of the above flood risk mitigation measures.	

References

ABI (2002a). *Statement on Principles on the Provision of Flooding Insurance*. Association of British Insurers, London.

ABI (2002b). *Development Planning and Flood Risk (PPG25): Association of British Insurers Guidance on Insurance Issues*. Association of British Insurers, London.

ACREMAN, M (2003). "The impact of floodplain restoration on flood hydrology". Proc 38th DEFRA Flood & coastal Management Conf. 6.1.1–6.1.11.

ADAS (1980). *The Design of Field Drainage Pipe Systems*. Reference Book 345, MAFF Agricultural Development and Advisory Service, HMSO, London.

ADAS (1984). *Arterial Drainage and Agriculture*. Drainage Leaflet No.16, MAFF Agricultural Development and Advisory Service. HMSO, London.

AMERICAN SOCIETY OF CIVIL ENGINEERS (1998). *Flood Resistant Design and Construction*, ASCE Standard SEI/ASCE 24–98.

BAYLISS, A C and REED, D W (2001). *The Use of Historical Data in Flood Frequency Estimation Report to MAFF*, Centre for Ecology & Hydrology, Wallingford.

BESLEY, P (1999). *Overtopping of Seawalls: Design and Assessment Manual*, Environment Agency R&D Technical Report W178, Environment Agency.

BOARDMAN, J (1995). "Damage to property by runoff from agricultural land, South Downs, southern England, 1976–93". *The Geographical Journal*, vol 161, no 2, July, pp 177–191.

BOORMAN, D B; HOLLIS, J M and LILLY, A (1995). *Hydrology of Soil Types: a Hydrologically-based Classification of the Soils of the United Kingdom*. Institute of Hydrology Report no 126, Wallingford.

BUILDING RESEARCH ESTABLISHMENT SCOTTISH LABORATORY (1996). *Design Guidance on Flood Damage to Dwellings*. HMSO for the Scottish Office Construction and Building Control Group, Edinburgh.

BYE, P and HORNER, M (1998). *Easter 1998 floods: final assessment by the independent review team*, Environment Agency.

CIRIA (1995). *Water-resisting basements*. R139, CIRIA, London.

COSLA (2003). *Final Report of the Committee of Scottish Local Authorities (COSLA) Flooding Task Group*, COSLA.

CRICHTON, D (2003). *Flood Risk and Insurance in England and Wales: Are There Lessons to be Learned from Scotland?* Benfield Craig Hazard Research Centre, Technical Paper 1.

CROWDER, R A (2003). *Benchmarking and Scoping of Hydraulic River Models*, Environment Agency Research and Technical Report, W5-105/TR2, Environment Agency.

Defra (2003). "Supplementary Guidance: Climate change considerations for flood and coastal management", unpublished.

DEPARTMENT OF THE ENVIRONMENT (1992). *Planning Policy Guidance Note 20: Coastal Planning*, HMSO, London.

DIXON and TAWN (1997). *Spatial Analysis for the UK Coast*, Proudman Oceanographic Laboratory Internal Document 112.

DTLR (2001). *Planning Policy Guidance Note 25: Development and Flood Risk*, HMSO, London.

EGLI, T (2002). *Non Structural Flood Plain Management: Measures and Their Effectiveness*, International Commission for the Protection of the Rhine.

ELLIOTT, C R N and LEGGETT, D J (2001). *Reducing the impacts of flooding – extemporary measures*, FR/IP/45, CIRIA, London.

ENVIRONMENT AGENCY (1999a). "Development and Flood Risk: Internal guidance on Planning Application Responses", unpublished.

ENVIRONMENT AGENCY (1999b). "Flood Defence Information Sheet No.4: Culverts", unpublished.

ENVIRONMENT AGENCY (1999c). "Flood Defence Information Sheet No.5: Bridges", unpublished.

ENVIRONMENT AGENCY (2001). *Lessons learned: Autumn 2000 floods*.

ENVIRONMENT AGENCY (2002). *Trash Screens Design and Operations Manual*, R&D Report W5A-01.

ENVIRONMENT AGENCY (2003a). *East Coast Floods 50th Anniversary Leaflet*.

ENVIRONMENT AGENCY (2003b). *National Standing Advice to Local Planning Authorities for Planning Applications: Development and Flood Risk: User Guidance Note*.

ENVIRONMENT AGENCY (2003c). *Flood Mapping Strategy*.

EUROPEAN UNION (2000). *Directive 2000/60/EC of the European Parliament and of the Council establishing a framework for the Community action in the field of water policy* (Water Framework Directive).

FARQUHARSON, F A K; MACKNEY, D; NEWSON, M D and THOMASSON, A J (1978). *Estimation of Run-off Potential of River Catchments from Soil Surveys*, Special Survey No.11, Soil Survey of England and Wales, Lawes Agricultural Trust, Harpenden.

FISHER, K and RAMSBOTTOM, D (2001) *River Diversions: A Design Guide*, HR Wallingford.

FLEMING, G (2001). *Learning to Live with Rivers*. "Final Report of the Institution of Civil Engineers' Presidential Commission to Review the Technical Aspects of Flood Risk Management in England and Wales", Institution of Civil Engineers, London.

HALL, M J; HOCKIN, D L and ELLIS, J B (1993). *Design of flood storage reservoirs*. B14, CIRIA, London. 187 pp.

HAMER, B; WEBB, D; DALE, W and HOME, R (2000). Improved methodology for predicting flood limits in coastal regions. Conf Proc 35th MAFF River and Coastal Engineers, 02.3, pp 1–12.

HASSELL, J M; BOORMAN, D; MCDONALD, R and HILL, S (2002). *Climate Change Scenarios for the United Kingdom: The UKCIP02 Scientific Report*. Tyndall Centre for Climate Change Research, School of Environmental Sciences, University of East Anglia, Norwich, UK, 120 pp.

HAWKES, P; WADE, S and REYNARD, N (2002). UKCIP02 climate change scenarios: implementation for flood and coastal defence. Con Proc 37th Defra Flood & Coastal Management, 02.2.1 – 02.2.11.

HIGHWAYS AGENCY (1995). *Design Manual for Roads and Bridges. Volume 4 Geotechnics and drainage, Section 2 Drainage, Part 1: HA 71/95: The effects on flooding of highway construction on flood plains*, London, HMSO.

HR WALLINGFORD (2003a). *Guide to the Management of Flood Plains to Reduce Flood Risks, Stage 1: Development Draft*. Defra/Environment Agency, SR 599, HR Wallingford, Wallingford.

HR WALLINGFORD (2003b). *Preliminary Rainfall Runoff Management for Developments: User Guide*. SR 637, HR Wallingford, Wallingford.

HUGHES, A; HEWLETT, H; SAMUELS, P; MORRIS, M; SAYERS, P; MOFFAT, I; HARDING, A and TEDD, P (2000). *Risk management for UK reservoirs*. C542, CIRIA. London.

HULME, M; JENKINS, J; LU, X; TURNPENNY, J R; MITCHELL, T D; JONES, R G; LOWE, J; MURPHY, J M; HASSELL, D; BOORMAN, P; McDONALD, R and HILL, S (2002). *Climate Change Scenarios for the United Kingdom: The UKCIP02 Scientific Report*. Tyndall Centre for Climate Change Research, School of Environmental Sciences, University of East Anglia, Norwich. 120 pp.

INSTITUTE OF HYDROLOGY (1999). *Flood Estimation Handbook*. Institute of Hydrology. Wallingford.

KELLAGHER, R (2004). *Drainage of Development Sites – A guide*. SR 574, HR Wallingford, Wallingford.

KIRBY, A M and ASH, J R (2000). *Fluvial Freeboard Guidance Note*. R&D Technical Report W187, Environment Agency. WRc, Swindon.

KOHLI, A and HAGER, W H (2001). "Building scour in flood plains". *Proc Institution of Civil Engineers, Water and Maritime Engineering* 148. June 2, pp 61–80.

McCARTNEY, M P and NADEN, P S (1995). "A semi-empirical investigation of the influence of flood-plain storage on flood flow". *Journal of the Chartered Institution of Water and Environmental Management*, 9 June, pp 236–246.

McCONNELL, K (1998). *Revetment Systems Against Wave Attack – a Design Manual*, Thomas Telford, London.

McPHERSON, I (2002). "Flooding – Part One: Planning and development plans". *Planning Inspectorate Journal*, vol 24.

MARSHALL, D C W and BAYLISS, A C (1994). *Flood Estimation for Small Catchments*. Institute of Hydrology Report no124, Wallingford.

MARTIN, P; TURNER, B; WADDINGTON, K; DELL, J; PRATT, C; CAMPBELL, N; PAYNE, J and REED, B (2000a). *Sustainable urban drainage systems: design manual for Scotland and Northern Ireland*. C521, CIRIA, London.

MARTIN, P; TURNER, B; WADDINGTON, K; DELL, J; PRATT, C; CAMPBELL, N; PAYNE, J and REED, B (2000b). *Sustainable urban drainage systems: design manual for England and Wales*. C522, CIRIA, London.

MARTIN, P; TURNER, B; DELL, J; PAYNE, J; ELLIOT, C and REED, B (2001). *Sustainable urban drainage systems: best practice manual for England, Scotland, Wales and Northern Ireland*. C523, CIRIA, London.

MAY, R W P; ACKERS, J C and KIRBY, A M (2002). *Manual on scour at bridges and other hydraulic structures*. C551, CIRIA, London.

MAY, R W P; MARTIN, P and PRICE, N J (1998). *Low-Cost Options for Prevention of Flooding from sewers*. C506, CIRIA, London.

MOORE, V (2002). *A Practical Approach to Planning Law*, 8th edition, Oxford University Press.

NATIONAL AUDIT OFFICE (2001). *Inland Flood Defence*: Report by the Comptroller and Auditor general, HC 299, Session 2000–2001: 15 March 2001. National Audit Office.

NATIONAL ASSEMBLY FOR WALES (1998). *Technical Advice Note (Wales) 15 Development and Flood Risk*. National Assembly for Wales, Cardiff.

NATIONAL ASSEMBLY FOR WALES (2002). *Planning Policy Wales Chapter 13 – Minimising and Managing Environmental Risks and Pollution*. National Assembly for Wales, Cardiff.

NATIONAL ASSEMBLY FOR WALES (2003a). *Technical Advice Note (Wales) 15: Development and Flood Risk*. Consultation Draft, July 2003. National Assembly for Wales, Cardiff.

NATIONAL ASSEMBLY FOR WALES (2003b). *Technical Advice Note (Wales) 15: Development and Flood Risk*. Consultation Draft, July 2003, Corrigenda. National Assembly for Wales, Cardiff.

NERC (1976). *Flood Studies Report*, Natural Environment Research Council, London.

ODPM (2002). *Preparing for Floods*, HMSO, London.

OGUNYOYE, F and VAN HEEREVELD, M (2002). *Temporary and Demountable Flood Protection: Interim Guidance on Use*. Defra/Environment Agency, R&D publication 130,

Environment Agency.

PENNING-ROWSELL, E; JOHNSON, C; TUNSTALL, S; TAPSELL, S; MORRIS, J; CHATTERTON, J; COKER, A and GREEN, C (2003). *The Benefits of Flood and Coastal Defence*: Techniques and Data for 2003. Flood Hazard Research Centre, Middlesex University. 322 pp.

PRICE, D J and McINALLY, G (2001). *Climate Change: Review of Levels of Protection Offered by Flood Prevention Systems*. Scottish Executive Central Research Unit Report. The Stationery Office, Edinburgh.

RAMSBOTTOM, D; DAY, R and RICKARD, C (1997). *Culvert design manual*. R168, CIRIA, London.

RIVER RESTORATION CENTRE (2002). *Manual of River Restoration Techniques 2002 Update*. River Restoration Centre, Silsoe.

ROBINSON, V; SOLOMON, J and MORRIS, S (2001). *Groundwater Flooding in the Thames Region Winter 2001*. Environment Agency Thames Region, Reading, October 2001.

SCOTTISH ENVIRONMENT PROTECTION AGENCY (in prep). "National Drainage Impact Assessment Guidelines".

SCOTTISH ENVIRONMENT PROTECTION AGENCY (2000). *SEPA Policy 41. Development at Risk of Flooding: Advice and Consultation*.

SCOTTISH EXECUTIVE (2001). *Planning Advice Note (PAN) 61 Planning and Sustainable Urban Drainage Systems*.

SCOTTISH EXECUTIVE (2004). *Scottish Planning Policy SPP7 Planning and Flooding*.

SCOTTISH OFFICE (1995). *National Planning Policy Guideline 7 – Planning And Flooding*, The Scottish Office.

SIMM, J D; BRAMPTON, A H; BEECH, N W and BROOKE, J S (1996). *Beach management manual*. R153, CIRIA, London.

SIMPSON, B; BLOWER, T; CRAIG, R N and WILKINSON, W B, (1989). *The engineering implications of rising groundwater in the deep aquifer below London*. SP69, CIRIA, London.

TAPSELL, S M; PENNING-ROWSELL, E C; TUNSTALL, S M and WILSON, T L (2002). "Vulnerability to flooding: health and social dimensions". *Flood Risk in a Changing Climate*. Special Edition of Philosophical Transactions of the Royal Society of London, Mathematical, Physical and Engineering Sciences, 360, 1796, pp 1511–1526.

THOMAS, F (1995). "Principles of flood plain management". In: (J.Gariner *et al*, eds) *Defence from Floods and Flood Plain Management*, pp 257–270. Kluwer Academic Publishings.

WARD, D; HOLES, N and JOSÉ, P (eds), (1994). *The New Rivers and Wildlife Handbook*, Royal Society for the Protection of Birds. Sandy.

WHO (2002). *Floods: Climate Change and Adaptation Strategies for Human Health.* Report on a WHO meeting, London, 30 June–2 July 2002. World Health Organisation, Copenhagen.

WILKINSON, W B and BRASSINGTON, F C (1991). "Rising groundwater levels – an international problem". In: (R.A. Downing and W.B. Wilkinson, eds) *Applied Groundwater Hydrology.* Clarendon Press, Oxford. pp 35–53.

WORTH, D and COX, R (2000) Tidal flood risk areas – simply credible. *35th MAFF Conf Proc River and Coastal Engineers,* 02.2, pp 1–10.